Graded examples in r

CH00656216

Algebra
Answers

M. R. Heylings M.A., M.Sc.

Schofield & Sims Limited   Huddersfield

0 7217 2326 8

First printed 1982
Reprinted 1985
Reprinted 1987
Reprinted 1989

The series **Graded examples in mathematics**
comprises:

Fractions and Decimals	0 7217 2323 3
Answer Book	0 7217 2324 1
Algebra	0 7217 2325 x
Answer Book	0 7217 2326 8
Area and Volume	0 7217 2327 6
Answer Book	0 7217 2328 4
General Arithmetic	0 7217 2329 2
Answer Book	0 7217 2330 6
Geometry and Trigonometry	0 7217 2331 4
Answer Book	0 7217 2332 2
Negative Numbers and Graphs	0 7217 2333 0
Answer Book	0 7217 2334 9
Matrices and Transformations	0 7217 2335 7
Answer Book	0 7217 2336 5
Sets, Probability and Statistics	0 7217 2337 3
Answer Book	0 7217 2338 1
Revision of Topics	0 7217 2339 x
Answer Book	0 7217 2340 3

Designed by Peter Sinclair (Design and Print) Ltd, Wetherby

Printed in England by Pindar Print Limited, Scarborough, North Yorkshire.

Contents

Balancing and Equations

Simplification and Substitution

Further Equations

Simultaneous Equations

Expansions and Factors

Quadratic Equations

Inequalities

Formulae

Fractions in Algebra

Balancing and Equations

Mobiles

Balancing

Simple equations

Mobiles

The three mobiles are intended for class discussion. Note that in all three problems, the arms of each balance are of equal length. The idea of a balance being maintained on each of two arms is a preliminary visual aid to understanding simple equations.

1 **a** 10 grams   **b** 5 grams   **c** 20 grams   **d** 20 grams   **e** 50 grams
   f 25 grams   **g** 15 grams   **h** $7\frac{1}{2}$ grams   **i** $2\frac{1}{2}$ grams   **j** $7\frac{1}{2}$ grams

2 40 grams, 50 grams, 55 grams, 25 grams

3 8 grams, 2 grams, 5 grams, $3\frac{1}{2}$ grams, $2\frac{1}{2}$ grams

Balancing

Part 1

In problem 7, for the first time, the idea of "taking something from both sides" can be used. One triangle can be cut from each side and a balance will still be maintained.
In problem 8, two circles can be taken from both sides.

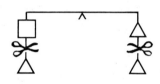

1 8	**2** 9	**3** 12	**4** 3	**5** 3	**6** 6
7 6	**8** 3	**9** 10	**10** 2	**11** 4	**12** $3\frac{1}{2}$
13 3	**14** 6	**15** $3\frac{1}{2}$	**16** $2\frac{1}{2}$	**17** $3\frac{1}{2}$	**18** 0
19 $1\frac{1}{2}$	**20** 5				

Part 2

1 4, 8	**2** 10, 20	**3** 6, 12	**4** 4, 10	**5** 2, 2	**6** 6, 12
7 3, $4\frac{1}{2}$	**8** 3, 6	**9** 3, $1\frac{1}{2}$	**10** 3, 0	**11** 0, 6	**12** 0, 4
13 6, 3	**14** 3, 6	**15** $2\frac{1}{2}$, 5	**16** 4, 6		

Part 3

These diagrams provide a visual step towards the symbolism of an "equation".

1 3	**2** 5	**3** 2	**4** 1	**5** 2	**6** 1
7 5	**8** 4	**9** 3	**10** 3	**11** 5	**12** 3
13 4	**14** 4	**15** 4	**16** 3	**17** 4	**18** 1
19 $2\frac{1}{2}$	**20** $2\frac{1}{2}$	**21** 1	**22** 1	**23** 3	**24** 5
25 7	**26** 7	**27** 3	**28** 5	**29** 4	**30** 4
31 4	**32** 3	**33** 5	**34** 2	**35** 5	**36** 2
37 2	**38** 2	**39** 2	**40** $4\frac{1}{2}$		

Balancing

Part 4

1 3	**2** 2	**3** 3	**4** 2	**5** 4	**6** 2
7 1	**8** $3\frac{1}{2}$	**9** $1\frac{1}{2}$	**10** $1\frac{1}{4}$	**11** 7	**12** 5
13 4	**14** 5	**15** 2	**16** 1	**17** 5	**18** $3\frac{1}{2}$
19 2	**20** $3\frac{1}{2}$	**21** 3	**22** 2	**23** 3	**24** 3
25 1	**26** $\frac{1}{2}$	**27** 2	**28** $\frac{1}{3}$	**29** $1\frac{1}{3}$	**30** $1\frac{1}{2}$
31 $3\frac{1}{3}$	**32** $3\frac{1}{4}$	**33** $\frac{1}{2}$	**34** $\frac{1}{3}$	**35** $\frac{1}{2}$	**36** $1\frac{1}{4}$
37 $1\frac{1}{5}$	**38** $\frac{5}{7}$				

Simple equations

Part 1

1 $x = 2$	**2** $x = 9$	**3** $x = 1$	**4** $x = 2$	**5** $x = 12$
6 $x = 9$	**7** $x = 1$	**8** $x = 2$	**9** $x = 1$	**10** $x = 2$
11 $x = 3$	**12** $x = 4$	**13** $x = 7$	**14** $x = 11$	**15** $x = 4$
16 $x = 0$	**17** $x = 1$	**18** $x = 7$	**19** $x = 4$	**20** $x = 12$

Part 2

1 $x = 9$	**2** $x = 9$	**3** $x = 7$	**4** $x = 10$	**5** $x = 17$
6 $x = 8$	**7** $x = 4\frac{1}{2}$	**8** $x = 7$	**9** $x = 6$	**10** $x = 11$
11 $x = 14$	**12** $x = 12$	**13** $x = 5\frac{1}{2}$	**14** $x = 11$	**15** $x = 11$
16 $x = 7$	**17** $x = 5$	**18** $x = \frac{1}{2}$	**19** $x = 5$	**20** $x = 5$

Part 3

1 $x = 5$	**2** $x = 4$	**3** $x = 2$	**4** $x = 9$	**5** $x = 7$
6 $x = 2$	**7** $x = 11$	**8** $x = 5$	**9** $x = 5$	**10** $x = 5$
11 $x = 12$	**12** $x = 7$	**13** $x = 6$	**14** $x = 8$	**15** $x = 32$
16 $x = 34$	**17** $x = 29$	**18** $x = 36$	**19** $x = 64$	**20** $x = 109$

Part 4

1 $x = 10$	**2** $x = 12$	**3** $x = 8$	**4** $x = 18$	**5** $x = 14$
6 $x = 20$	**7** $x = 60$	**8** $x = 18$	**9** $x = 32$	**10** $x = 45$
11 $x = 7$	**12** $x = 15$	**13** $x = 48$	**14** $x = 65$	**15** $x = 46$
16 $x = 72$	**17** $x = 72$	**18** $x = 224$	**19** $x = 100$	**20** $x = 174$

Simple equations

Part 5

1 $x = 1$	**2** $x = 15$	**3** $x = 4$	**4** $x = 6$	**5** $x = 7$
6 $x = 7$	**7** $x = 18$	**8** $x = 15$	**9** $x = 11$	**10** $x = 2$
11 $x = 18$	**12** $x = 4$	**13** $x = 16$	**14** $x = 11$	**15** $x = 10$
16 $x = 15$	**17** $x = 16$	**18** $x = 13$	**19** $x = 27$	**20** $x = 28$
21 $x = 5$	**22** $x = 11$	**23** $x = 12$	**24** $x = 18$	**25** $x = 4$
26 $x = 5$	**27** $x = 20$	**28** $x = 9$	**29** $x = 7$	**30** $x = 3$
31 $x = 36$	**32** $x = 13$			

Part 6

1 $x = 3$	**2** $x = 5$	**3** $x = 3$	**4** $x = 2$	**5** $x = 4$
6 $x = 5$	**7** $x = 3\frac{1}{2}$	**8** $x = 2\frac{1}{2}$	**9** $x = 5$	**10** $x = 3$
11 $x = 4$	**12** $x = 3$	**13** $x = 5\frac{1}{2}$	**14** $x = 10$	**15** $x = 1\frac{1}{4}$
16 $x = 4\frac{1}{2}$	**17** $x = 3\frac{1}{2}$	**18** $x = 10$	**19** $x = 12$	**20** $x = 8$

Part 7

Brackets can be introduced as "so many lots of" or "so many bags of" and the equation $2(x + 3) = 16$ could even be drawn visually as

1 $x = 5$	**2** $x = 2$	**3** $x = 2$	**4** $x = 3$	**5** $x = 3$
6 $x = 4$	**7** $x = 5$	**8** $x = 3$	**9** $x = 1$	**10** $x = 2\frac{1}{2}$
11 $x = 1$	**12** $x = 10$	**13** $x = 6$	**14** $x = 6$	**15** $x = 12$
16 $x = 2$	**17** $x = 5$	**18** $x = 1$	**19** $x = 1\frac{1}{2}$	**20** $x = 4$

Part 8

1 $x = 6$	**2** $x = 8$	**3** $x = 4$	**4** $x = 3$	**5** $x = 6$
6 $x = 4$	**7** $x = 2\frac{1}{2}$	**8** $x = 4\frac{1}{2}$	**9** $x = 6$	**10** $x = 1\frac{1}{2}$
11 $x = 2$	**12** $x = 3$	**13** $x = 10$	**14** $x = 2\frac{1}{2}$	**15** $x = 4\frac{1}{2}$
16 $x = 7$	**17** $x = 3\frac{1}{2}$	**18** $x = 10$	**19** $x = 20$	**20** $x = 13\frac{1}{3}$

Part 9

1 $x = 3$	**2** $x = 3$	**3** $x = 4$	**4** $x = 6$	**5** $x = 3$
6 $x = 4\frac{1}{2}$	**7** $x = 4\frac{1}{2}$	**8** $x = 2$	**9** $x = 5\frac{1}{2}$	**10** $x = 2\frac{1}{2}$
11 $x = 2$	**12** $x = 2$	**13** $x = 3$	**14** $x = 13$	**15** $x = 8\frac{1}{2}$
16 $x = 9\frac{1}{3}$	**17** $x = 5\frac{1}{4}$	**18** $x = 3$	**19** $x = 3$	**20** $x = 4\frac{1}{2}$

Simple equations

Part 10

1	$x = 2$	2	$x = 3$	3	$x = 2$	4	$x = 7$	5	$x = 2$
6	$x = 3$	7	$x = 3$	8	$x = 6$	9	$x = 3$	10	$x = 4$
11	$x = 5$	12	$x = 1\frac{1}{2}$	13	$x = 2\frac{1}{4}$	14	$x = 0$	15	$\frac{2}{3}$
16	$x = 1\frac{2}{5}$	17	$x = 4$	18	$x = 44$	19	$x = 20$	20	11

Part 11

1	$x = 3$	2	$x = 2$	3	$x = 4$	4	$x = 9$	5	$x = 3$
6	$x = 2$	7	$x = 4$	8	$x = 2$	9	$x = 1$	10	$x = 2\frac{1}{2}$
11	$x = 3\frac{1}{2}$	12	$x = 7$	13	$x = 7$	14	$x = 3$	15	$x = 4$
16	$x = 3$	17	$x = 3$	18	$x = 3$	19	$x = 8\frac{1}{2}$	20	$x = 3\frac{1}{2}$

Part 12

1	$x = 6$	2	$x = 6$	3	$x = 3$	4	$x = 4$	5	$x = 4$
6	$x = 2$	7	$x = 2$	8	$x = 5$	9	$x = 6$	10	$x = 2$
11	$x = 1\frac{1}{2}$	12	$x = 7\frac{1}{2}$	13	$x = 2\frac{1}{2}$	14	$x = 3\frac{1}{4}$	15	$x = 3\frac{1}{2}$
16	$x = 4\frac{1}{2}$	17	$x = 4$	18	$x = 5$	19	$x = 3$	20	$x = 2$

Part 13

1	$x = 2$	2	$x = 5$	3	$x = 2$	4	$x = 7$	5	$x = 6\frac{1}{2}$
6	$x = \frac{1}{2}$	7	$x = 11$	8	$x = 9$	9	$x = 10$	10	$x = 5\frac{1}{2}$
11	$x = 8$	12	$x = 3$	13	$x = 3\frac{1}{4}$	14	$x = 8\frac{1}{2}$	15	$x = 5\frac{1}{2}$
16	$x = 10\frac{1}{3}$	17	$x = 6$	18	$x = 1\frac{3}{4}$	19	$x = 6\frac{2}{3}$	20	$x = 4$

Part 14

1	$x = 3$	2	$x = 10$	3	$x = 2$	4	$x = 2$	5	$x = 2$
6	$x = 2$	7	$x = 3$	8	$x = 3$	9	$x = 4$	10	$x = 8$
11	$x = 5$	12	$x = 5\frac{1}{2}$	13	$x = 2$	14	$x = 6\frac{1}{2}$	15	$x = 4$
16	$x = 4\frac{1}{2}$	17	$x = 7$	18	$x = 6$	19	$x = 21$	20	$x = 4\frac{1}{2}$

Simplification and Substitution

Simplifying expressions
Simple substitution
Substitution into formulae
Further practice

Simplifying expressions

1 $12a$		**2** $9b$		**3** $8c$		**4** $11d$		**5** $2e$	
6 $2f$		**7** $2x$		**8** $4y$		**9** z		**10** $5x$	
11 $2y$		**12** 0		**13** $7a + 6b$		**14** $9x + 7y$		**15** $6m + 9n$	
16 $9a + 2b$		**17** $3x + 3y$		**18** $p + 3q$		**19** $y + 3z$		**20** $5s + 4t$	
21 0		**22** 0		**23** $m + 4n$		**24** $2y$		**25** $2e$	
26 $3b$		**27** $5x + 2y$		**28** $5a + 3c$		**29** $a + c$		**30** $4n + p$	

31 $-2s$ **32** $4r$ **33** $8y + 7z$ **34** $3a + 10b + 15c$

35 $11e + 3f + g$ **36** 0

37 $21x + 14y$ **38** $14x + 14y$ **39** $26x + 6y$ **40** $23x + y$

41 $7x + y$ **42** $14x$ **43** $9n$ **44** $7p + 2q$

45 $a + 27b$ **46** $6y$ **47** $9r + 7s$ **48** $11p + q$

49 $11s + 5u$ **50** $3a + 17b$ **51** $24n$ **52** $5t$

53 $3x + 9y$ **54** $17f$ **55** 0 **56** $10m + 42k$

57 $10a$ **58** $5p + 14q$ **59** $17b$ **60** $20x$

Simple substitution

1 10	**2** 12	**3** 23	**4** 13	**5** 9	**6** 16	**7** 14
8 6	**9** 0	**10** 0	**11** 3	**12** 4	**13** 6	**14** 7
15 3	**16** 1	**17** 0	**18** 1	**19** 5	**20** 8	**21** 39
22 30	**23** 28	**24** 27	**25** 33	**26** 20	**27** 30	**28** 27
29 25	**30** 11	**31** 29	**32** 4	**33** 29	**34** 22	**35** 24
36 45	**37** 32	**38** 20	**39** 13	**40** 20	**41** 19	**42** 14
43 0	**44** 2					

45 100	**46** 76	**47** 74	**48** 28	**49** 13	**50** 19	**51** 11
52 26	**53** 17	**54** 43	**55** 53	**56** 14	**57** 3	**58** 1
59 89	**60** 90					

Substitution into formulae

1 a	190	b	140	c	340	**2** a	34	b	88	c	60
3 a	55	b	350	c	850	**4** a	42	b	31	c	66
5 a	100	b	160	c	370	**6** a	88	b	101	c	75
7 a	63	b	67	c	86	**8** a	132	b	141	c	129
9 a	52	b	100	c	92	**10** a	380	b	590	c	840
11 a	128	b	405	c	1070	**12** a	256	b	432	c	528
13 a	$2\frac{1}{2}$	b	$2\frac{1}{10}$	c	$1\frac{2}{3}$	**14** a	6	b	12	c	$10\frac{1}{2}$
15 a	22	b	54	c	210	**16** a	60	b	132	c	248
17 a	11	b	10	c	13	**18** a	12	b	5	c	12
19 a	40	b	75	c	45	**20** a	110	b	84	c	$61\frac{1}{2}$

Further practice

Part 1

1 $6ab$	**2** $15mn$	**3** $21pq$	**4** $10xy$	**5** $20ab$	
6 $10yz$	**7** $24abc$	**8** $24mnp$	**9** $15pqr$	**10** $12abc$	
11 $40pqr$	**12** $30abc$				

13 $8ab$	**14** $15yz$	**15** $14mn$	**16** $12xy$	**17** $18st$
18 $30abc$	**19** $24xyz$	**20** $75tuv$	**21** $40abc$	**22** $18xyz$
23 $20xyz$	**24** $8pqr$	**25** $6stu$	**26** $12mnp$	**27** $4pqr$
28 $126abc$	**29** $8xy$	**30** $15xy$		

31 $6ab + 4ac$	**32** $12xy + 6xz$	**33** $10mp - 20mq$
34 $6st - 18su$	**35** $12ab + 4ac$	**36** $4pq + 2pr$
37 $4xy - 8xz$	**38** $3ab + 4ac$	**39** $4mx - 3my$
40 $8xa + 12x$	**41** $2st - 8s$	**42** $10ab - 15a$
43 $12mn + 18m$	**44** $15xy - 10xz$	**45** $8p^2 - 4pr$
46 $6ab + 7ac$	**47** $3xy - 2xz$	**48** $2xy + 3x$
49 $9ab + 7ac$	**50** $11xy + 10xz$	**51** $2mp + 2mq$
52 $7ax + 3ay$	**53** $3su$	**54** $3az + 6ay$
55 $9xy + 2xz$	**56** $12su + 5sv$	**57** $2mx + 10my$
58 $4ab + 7ac$	**59** $7xy$	**60** 0

Part 2

1 30	**2** 30	**3** 24	**4** 30	**5** 90	**6** 38
7 52	**8** 2	**9** 40	**10** 33	**11** 22	**12** 1
13 0	**14** 58	**15** 42	**16** 47	**17** 78	**18** 18
19 12	**20** 24	**21** 20	**22** 12	**23** 42	**24** 32
25 24	**26** 14	**27** 13	**28** 6	**29** 30	**30** 13
31 24	**32** 22	**33** 2	**34** 54	**35** 31	**36** 2
37 30	**38** 15	**39** 36	**40** 21	**41** 24	**42** 0
43 27	**44** 19	**45** 8	**46** 22	**47** 21	**48** 50
49 15	**50** 120	**51** 84	**52** 11		

Part 3

1 $x = 2$	**6** $x = 4\frac{2}{3}$	**11** $x = 5$	**16** $x = 2$
2 $x = 2$	**7** $x = 2\frac{1}{2}$	**12** $x = 6$	**17** $x = 1$
3 $x = 2$	**8** $x = 2$	**13** $x = 6\frac{1}{2}$	**18** $x = 2\frac{1}{2}$
4 $x = 1\frac{1}{2}$	**9** $x = 3$	**14** $x = 2\frac{1}{2}$	**19** $x = 9$
5 $x = 10$	**10** $x = 6$	**15** $x = 5$	**20** $x = 2\frac{1}{2}$

Further practice

21 $x = 6$	**24** $x = 3$	**27** $x = 5$	**30** $x = 2$
22 $x = 3$	**25** $x = 2$	**28** $x = 1$	**31** $x = 8\frac{1}{2}$
23 $x = 4$	**26** $x = 3$	**29** $x = 1$	**32** $x = 1\frac{1}{2}$
33 $x = 2\frac{1}{2}$	**40** $x = 4\frac{1}{2}$	**47** $x = 4$	**54** $x = 3\frac{1}{2}$
34 $x = \frac{1}{2}$	**41** $x = 7$	**48** $x = 2$	**55** $x = 2$
35 $x = 19$	**42** $x = 1$	**49** $x = 0$	**56** $x = 2\frac{1}{2}$
36 $x = 10$	**43** $x = 1$	**50** $x = 4$	**57** $x = 6$
37 $x = 1$	**44** $x = 11$	**51** $x = 0$	**58** $x = 2\frac{1}{2}$
38 $x = 1\frac{1}{2}$	**45** $x = 7\frac{1}{5}$	**52** $x = \frac{1}{2}$	**59** $x = 2\frac{1}{2}$
39 $x = 4\frac{1}{2}$	**46** $x = 0$	**53** $x = \frac{1}{2}$	**60** $x = \frac{1}{3}$

Further Equations

Negative numbers

A fuller treatment of negative numbers will be found in the book "Negative Numbers and Graphs".

Part 1

	a		b		c		d		e		f	
1	a	3°C	b	5°C	c	4°C	d	2°C	e	4°C	f	9°C
2	a	100 m	b	200 m	c	200 m	d	250 m	e	350 m	f	50 m

3 7°C   **4** 7°C   **5** 12 m   **6** 1800 m   **7** 8 floors   **8** 52 years
9 59 years **10** 110 m **11** 35 years **12** 5°C   **13** 9°C   **14** 9°C
15 −8°C

Part 2

1 Newent	**2** Aston	**3** Kilcot	**4** Lea	**5** Kilcot
6 Highleadon	**7** Lea	**8** Highleadon	**9** Over	**10** Tibberton
11 Highleadon	**12** Weston	**13** Weston	**14** Pencraig	**15** Pencraig
16 Lea	**17** Ross	**18** Longlevens	**19** Gloucester	**20** Cheltenham
21 Upleadon	**22** Kilcot	**23** Highnam	**24** Kilcot	**25** Highnam
26 Home	**27** Home	**28** Newent	**29** Home	**30** Newent

31 +3   **32** +8   **33** −2   **34** −7   **35** −6   **36** +5
37 −7   **38** +2   **39** +8   **40** +2   **41** +1   **42** −3

Part 3 The Number Ladder

1 −2   **2** −1   **3** −3   **4** −1   **5** +3   **6** +6   **7** +1
8 −4   **9** −8   **10** 0   **11** +3   **12** +3   **13** +1   **14** +2
15 −5   **16** −3   **17** 0   **18** 0   **19** −1   **20** −5   **21** −5
22 −8   **23** −5   **24** −6   **25** −8   **26** +3
27 −2   **28** −2   **29** +6   **30** 0   **31** +3   **32** −2   **33** −14 **34** −4
35 +2   **36** +4   **37** −4   **38** +5   **39** −4   **40** −9   **41** +13 **42** −4

43
a true	b true	c false	d true	e true
f true	g true	h true	i true	j true
k true	l true	m false	n false	o false

44
a >	b <	c >	d <	e >
f >	g <	h >	i <	j >
k >	l <	m >	n <	o >

45
a $3x$	b $-2x$	c $-3x$	d $-x$	e $3x$	f $-4x$
g $-2y$	h $-3y$	i $-9y$	j $-3y$	k $-2y$	l 0
m $-6z$	n 0	o $6z$	p $4z$	q $-2z$	r $8z$
s $-5a$	t $-4a$	u $-b$	v b	w $-c$	x 0
y $-13d$	z $11d$				

Negative numbers

46	**a** $5a - 2b$	**b** $4c + 5d$	**c** $10e - 6f$	**d** $g - 2h$
	e $-2j$	**f** $3m - n$	**g** $3p - 2q$	**h** $9r + 3s$
	i $3t - 6s$	**j** $-5u$	**k** $5w - 6x$	**l** $7z - y$
	m $3b$	**n** $2d - 9c$	**o** $8f - 14e$	**p** $-g$
	q 0	**r** $7m - 6n$	**s** $3q - 2p$	**t** $7s - 3$
	u $3r + 1$	**v** $7 - 4t$	**w** $4 - u$	**x** $4 - 5v$
	y -14	**z** -4		

Equations with negatives

The instruction "take something from both sides" is useful in solving an equation such as $2x + 3 = -5$.

Some teachers initially encourage an intermediate line of written working to emphasise this; though after practice these additional -3's would be omitted. Mentioning the number ladder with the instruction "minus 5 take away 3" facilitates obtaining the -8.

$$2x + 3 = -5$$
$$ -3 \quad -3$$
$$2x = -8$$
$$x = -4$$

Part 1

1 $a = 1$	**2** $b = 0$	**3** $c = -1$	**4** $d = -2$	**5** $e = -3$
6 $f = -2$	**7** $g = -6$	**8** $h = 1$	**9** $i = -7$	**10** $j = -3$
11 $k = -7$	**12** $m = -5$	**13** $n = -7$	**14** $p = -5$	**15** $q = -7$
16 $r = -11$	**17** $m = 2$	**18** $k = -14$	**19** $n = -6$	**20** $s = -2$
21 $t = -4$	**22** $u = -9$	**23** $x = -7$	**24** $y = -3$	**25** $z = -5$

Part 2

1 $a = -2$	**2** $b = -3$	**3** $c = -1$	**4** $d = -2$	**5** $e = -2$
6 $x = -2$	**7** $y = 0$	**8** $z = -2$	**9** $s = -1$	**10** $f = -2$
11 $g = -\frac{1}{2}$	**12** $h = -1\frac{1}{2}$	**13** $i = 3\frac{1}{3}$	**14** $j = 1$	**15** $m = -2$
16 $n = -4\frac{1}{2}$	**17** $p = 0$	**18** $j = 8$	**19** $k = -12$	**20** $m = -8$
21 $n = -10$	**22** $p = -1\frac{1}{5}$	**23** $q = -6$	**24** $r = -16$	**25** $z = -10$

Part 3

1 $x = -3$	**2** $x = -1$	**3** $x = -2$	**4** $x = -2$	**5** $x = -2\frac{1}{2}$
6 $x = -4$	**7** $x = -3$	**8** $x = -2$	**9** $x = -3$	**10** $x = -2$
11 $x = -2\frac{1}{2}$	**12** $x = -3\frac{1}{2}$	**13** $x = -\frac{1}{2}$	**14** $x = -1$	**15** $x = -2$
16 $x = -2\frac{1}{4}$	**17** $x = -1$	**18** $x = 2\frac{1}{2}$	**19** $x = -3\frac{1}{2}$	**20** $x = -1\frac{3}{4}$
21 $x = -1$	**22** $x = -1$	**23** $x = -1\frac{1}{3}$	**24** $x = -\frac{1}{2}$	**25** $x = -1$

Equations with negatives

Part 4

1 $a = 5$	**2** $b = 3$	**3** $c = 2$	**4** $d = 1$	**5** $e = -2$
6 $x = 6$	**7** $y = 2$	**8** $z = 7$	**9** $m = -3$	**10** $f = 7$
11 $g = 5$	**12** $h = -2$	**13** $i = 1$	**14** $j = -2$	**15** $p = 8$
16 $q = 5$	**17** $r = -3$	**18** $u = -5$	**19** $k = 3$	**20** $m = 4$
21 $n = 7$	**22** $p = -2\frac{1}{2}$	**23** $q = -3\frac{1}{2}$	**24** $r = 2\frac{1}{2}$	**25** $p = -3\frac{1}{2}$

Part 5

1 $a = 4$	**2** $b = -2$	**3** $c = 2$	**4** $d = -1$	**5** $e = 2$
6 $s = 2$	**7** $t = 2$	**8** $v = 2$	**9** $x = 2\frac{1}{2}$	**10** $f = 1$
11 $g = -1$	**12** $h = 3\frac{1}{2}$	**13** $i = -1\frac{1}{2}$	**14** $j = -1$	**15** $m = \frac{1}{2}$
16 $n = -1$	**17** $x = \frac{1}{2}$	**18** $y = 2\frac{1}{2}$	**19** $k = 8$	**20** $m = -4$
21 $n = 12$	**22** $p = 0$	**23** $q = 9$	**24** $r = 25$	**25** $z = 8$

Part 6

1 $x = 3$	**2** $x = 7$	**3** $x = 6$	**4** $x = 3$	**5** $x = 2$
6 $x = 2$	**7** $x = 5$	**8** $x = -1$	**9** $x = 2$	**10** $x = 2$
11 $x = 1\frac{1}{2}$	**12** $x = 2\frac{1}{2}$	**13** $x = 2\frac{1}{3}$	**14** $x = -6$	**15** $x = 6\frac{1}{2}$
16 $x = 3$	**17** $x = 1$	**18** $x = 2$	**19** $x = 4$	**20** $x = -1$
21 $x = -3$	**22** $x = 4$	**23** $x = 16$	**24** $x = 8$	**25** $x = 16$

Part 7

1 $x = -3$	**2** $x = -5$	**3** $x = -3$	**4** $x = -11$	**5** $x = -3$
6 $x = -2$	**7** $x = -2$	**8** $x = -2$	**9** $x = 4$	**10** $x = 7$
11 $x = 4$	**12** $x = 4$	**13** $x = 4$	**14** $x = 2$	**15** $x = 1$
16 $x = -3$	**17** $x = -6$	**18** $x = -3$	**19** $x = 6$	**20** $x = 2$
21 $x = 2$	**22** $x = -2$	**23** $x = 1\frac{1}{2}$	**24** $x = 2$	**25** $x = 1$
26 $x = -\frac{1}{2}$	**27** $x = 3$	**28** $x = 3$	**29** $x = 4\frac{1}{2}$	**30** $x = 2$
31 $x = 2$	**32** $x = \frac{1}{2}$	**33** $x = -2$	**34** $x = -1$	**35** $x = 1$
36 $x = 3$	**37** $x = 4\frac{1}{2}$	**38** $x = 1$	**39** $x = -2$	**40** $x = 2$
41 $x = -2\frac{1}{2}$	**42** $x = -3$	**43** $x = -5$	**44** $x = -5$	**45** $x = -7$
46 $x = -4$	**47** $x = 2$	**48** $x = 2$	**49** $x = 2$	**50** $x = 5$
51 $x = 1$	**52** $x = 3$	**53** $x = -6$	**54** $x = 2\frac{1}{2}$	**55** $x = 3\frac{1}{2}$
56 $x = -16$	**57** $x = 9$	**58** $x = 20$	**59** $x = 18$	**60** $x = \frac{1}{8}$

Equations with negatives

Part 8

1 $x = 8$	**2** $x = 13\frac{1}{2}$	**3** $x = 4$	**4** $x = 1\frac{1}{5}$	**5** $x = 2$
6 $x = 9$	**7** $x = 2$	**8** $x = 2$	**9** $x = 1\frac{1}{2}$	**10** $x = 1\frac{1}{2}$
11 $x = 5$	**12** $x = -2$	**13** $x = -3$	**14** $x = -7$	**15** $x = 1$
16 $x = 2\frac{4}{5}$	**17** $x = -1$	**18** $x = -2$	**19** $x = -2$	**20** $x = 2$
21 $x = 3$	**22** $x = 7\frac{1}{2}$	**23** $x = -1$	**24** $x = -4$	**25** $x = -4$
26 $x = 2\frac{2}{3}$	**27** $x = -2\frac{1}{2}$	**28** $x = 2\frac{7}{16}$	**29** $x = 4$	**30** $x = 10\frac{1}{2}$
31 $x = -\frac{7}{8}$	**32** $x = 0$	**33** $x = 0$	**34** $x = \frac{5}{21}$	**35** $x = 4$
36 $x = -5\frac{4}{5}$				

Revision of simple equations

Part 1

1 $x = 4$	**2** $x = 2$	**3** $x = 10$	**4** $x = 7$	**5** $x = 0$
6 $x = -1$	**7** $x = -2$	**8** $x = -5$	**9** $x = 2$	**10** $x = 3$
11 $x = 5$	**12** $x = 2$	**13** $x = 4$	**14** $x = 7$	**15** $x = 2\frac{1}{2}$
16 $x = 3$	**17** $x = 2\frac{1}{2}$	**18** $x = -2$	**19** $x = -3$	**20** $x = -3$

Part 2

1 $x = 2$	**2** $x = 4$	**3** $x = 2$	**4** $x = 3$	**5** $x = 4$
6 $x = 0$	**7** $x = -3$	**8** $x = -4$	**9** $x = 2$	**10** $x = 2$
11 $x = 3$	**12** $x = 1$	**13** $x = 3$	**14** $x = 5$	**15** $x = 2\frac{1}{2}$
16 $x = 5\frac{1}{2}$	**17** $x = 0$	**18** $x = -1$	**19** $x = -3$	**20** $x = -2$

Part 3

1 $x = 2$	**2** $x = 2\frac{3}{5}$	**3** $x = 3\frac{1}{2}$	**4** $x = 3\frac{1}{3}$	**5** $x = 2$
6 $x = -2$	**7** $x = -1$	**8** $x = -1\frac{1}{2}$	**9** $x = -2$	**10** $x = -3$
11 $x = -2\frac{3}{4}$	**12** $x = 6$	**13** $x = 1\frac{2}{3}$	**14** $x = 1\frac{1}{2}$	**15** $x = -2$
16 $x = -2$	**17** $x = -8$	**18** $x = 16$	**19** $x = 4$	**20** $x = 30$

Part 4

1 $x = 7$	**2** $x = 6$	**3** $x = 11$	**4** $x = 5$	**5** $x = 4$
6 $x = 2$	**7** $x = 2$	**8** $x = 8$	**9** $x = 3$	**10** $x = 5$
11 $x = 5$	**12** $x = 6$	**13** $x = 4$	**14** $x = 6$	**15** $x = 6$
16 $x = 2$	**17** $x = 2$	**18** $x = 2$	**19** $x = 1\frac{1}{4}$	**20** $x = 1\frac{1}{2}$

Revision of simple equations

Part 5

1 $x = 7$	**2** $x = 6$	**3** $x = 5$	**4** $x = 4$	**5** $x = 8$
6 $x = 1\frac{1}{2}$	**7** $x = 3\frac{1}{3}$	**8** $x = 3\frac{1}{2}$	**9** $x = 3\frac{1}{2}$	**10** $x = 3\frac{1}{3}$
11 $x = 5\frac{1}{3}$	**12** $x = 2\frac{1}{2}$	**13** $x = 6$	**14** $x = 5$	**15** $x = 4$
16 $x = 3$	**17** $x = 1$	**18** $x = -2$	**19** $x = -1\frac{1}{2}$	**20** $x = -1\frac{1}{2}$

Part 6

1 $x = 2$	**2** $x = 10$	**3** $x = 6$	**4** $x = 12$	**5** $x = 2$
6 $x = 8$	**7** $x = -1$	**8** $x = 2$	**9** $x = -1$	**10** $x = 2$
11 $x = -2$	**12** $x = 3$	**13** $x = 1$	**14** $x = 8$	**15** $x = -8$
16 $x = -1$	**17** $x = 8$	**18** $x = 16$	**19** $x = 2\frac{1}{2}$	**20** $x = 1\frac{3}{5}$
21 $x = -3$	**22** $x = 3\frac{3}{4}$	**23** $x = 2\frac{1}{2}$	**24** $x = 12$	**25** $x = 24$
26 $x = 8$	**27** $x = 6$	**28** $x = -2$	**29** $x = 15$	**30** $x = -18$

More equations with brackets

Some familiarity with the multiplication of positive and negative numbers will be needed in some of these exercises, though the multiplication of two negative numbers occurs only in parts 7 and 8.

Part 1

1 $x = 1$	**2** $x = 3$	**3** $x = 4$	**4** $x = 1$	**5** $x = 2$
6 $x = 0$	**7** $x = 5$	**8** $x = 6$	**9** $x = 2\frac{1}{2}$	**10** $x = 2\frac{1}{2}$
11 $x = \frac{1}{2}$	**12** $x = 1\frac{1}{2}$			

Part 2

1 $x = 5$	**2** $x = 1$	**3** $x = \frac{1}{2}$	**4** $x = 1$	**5** $x = 2$
6 $x = 2$	**7** $x = 3$	**8** $x = 1$	**9** $x = 2$	**10** $x = -\frac{1}{5}$
11 $x = \frac{11}{19}$	**12** $x = 1\frac{1}{2}$			

Part 3

1 $x = 3$	**2** $x = 8$	**3** $x = 5$	**4** $x = 4$	**5** $x = 2$
6 $x = 2$	**7** $x = 5\frac{1}{2}$	**8** $x = 0$	**9** $x = 1$	**10** $x = 2\frac{2}{3}$
11 $x = 7\frac{1}{3}$	**12** $x = 1$			

More equations with brackets

Part 4

1 $x = 9$	**2** $x = 13$	**3** $x = 4\frac{1}{2}$	**4** $x = 6\frac{1}{2}$	**5** $x = 20$
6 $x = 10\frac{1}{2}$	**7** $x = 19$	**8** $x = 8\frac{1}{2}$	**9** $x = 0$	**10** $x = -5$
11 $x = 7$	**12** $x = 4$	**13** $x = 0$	**14** $x = 4$	**15** $x = 7$
16 $x = 2$	**17** $x = -2$	**18** $x = -5$	**19** $x = -5$	**20** $x = -1\frac{4}{5}$

Part 5

1 $x = 7$	**2** $x = 3\frac{1}{2}$	**3** $x = 7$	**4** $x = 12$	**5** $x = 3$
6 $x = 2\frac{2}{3}$	**7** $x = 8$	**8** $x = 3$	**9** $x = 8$	**10** $x = 0$
11 $x = \frac{1}{2}$	**12** $x = 1\frac{2}{5}$			

Part 6

1 $x = 3$	**2** $x = 6$	**3** $x = 3$	**4** $x = -1$	**5** $x = -3$
6 $x = -2$	**7** $x = 3\frac{1}{2}$	**8** $x = -\frac{2}{3}$	**9** $x = -5$	**10** $x = -1\frac{3}{4}$
11 $x = -2\frac{1}{2}$	**12** $x = 5$	**13** $x = -1\frac{1}{2}$	**14** $x = 2\frac{1}{4}$	**15** $x = -1$
16 $x = 2$	**17** $x = 4$	**18** $x = 1\frac{1}{4}$	**19** $x = -14$	**20** $x = -3$

Part 7

1 $x = 3$	**2** $x = 2$	**3** $x = 4$	**4** $x = 3$	**5** $x = 8$
6 $x = 3$	**7** $x = 6$	**8** $x = 6$	**9** $x = 6$	**10** $x = 1$
11 $x = 2$	**12** $x = -2$	**13** $x = 6$	**14** $x = 0$	**15** $x = -1$
16 $x = -1$	**17** $x = 3$	**18** $x = 4$	**19** $x = 2$	**20** $x = 4$
21 $x = 6$	**22** $x = 2$	**23** $x = 5$	**24** $x = 2\frac{1}{2}$	**25** $x = 4$
26 $x = 2\frac{1}{2}$	**27** $x = -\frac{1}{4}$	**28** $x = -2$	**29** $x = -\frac{1}{2}$	**30** $x = -2$

Part 8

1 $x = 5$	**2** $x = 2$	**3** $x = -3$	**4** $x = 5\frac{1}{2}$	**5** $x = 4$
6 $x = 1\frac{1}{3}$	**7** $x = 1\frac{3}{4}$	**8** $x = 18$	**9** $x = 4$	**10** $x = 5$
11 $x = 5\frac{1}{2}$	**12** $x = 2$	**13** $x = 3$	**14** $x = 0$	**15** $x = -3$
16 $x = -2$	**17** $x = 1$	**18** $x = 6$	**19** $x = 4\frac{2}{3}$	**20** $x = -4$
21 $x = -\frac{7}{8}$	**22** $x = 4$	**23** $x = 3$	**24** $x = 0$	**25** $x = 2\frac{1}{3}$
26 $x = 1$	**27** $x = 0$	**28** $x = 2\frac{2}{3}$	**29** $x = -2$	**30** $x = 0$

Forming equations

Part 1

1 **a** 50° **b** 40° **c** 35° **d** 35° **e** 70° **f** 30° **g** 50° **h** 25°

2 **a** 30° **b** 70° **c** 45° **d** 33°

3 **a** 35° **b** 60° **c** $32\frac{1}{2}$° **d** 80°

4 **a** 55° **b** 50° **c** $72\frac{1}{2}$° **d** 80°

5 **a** 40° **b** 60° **c** 60° **d** 20° **e** 40° **f** 20°

6 **a** 25° **b** 20° **c** 4° **d** 6° **e** $5\frac{1}{2}$°

7 **a** 5 **b** $2\frac{1}{2}$ **c** 9 **d** $3\frac{1}{2}$ **e** $\frac{1}{2}$ **f** 3 **g** 3 **h** $2\frac{1}{3}$
   i 8 **j** 22

8 **a** $3\frac{1}{2}$ **b** 2 **c** 4 **d** $3\frac{1}{3}$ **e** 3 **f** 4 **g** 5 **h** 5
   i 3 **j** 2 **k** 4 **l** 6 **m** $2\frac{1}{2}$ **n** 4

9 **a** 6 **b** 7

10 **a** $1\frac{1}{3}$ **b** 12

11 3

12 **a** 9 **b** 11 **c** $3\frac{1}{2}$ **d** $8\frac{1}{2}$ **e** $2\frac{1}{2}$ **f** 8 **g** 8 **h** 11
   i 40 **j** 66 **k** 12 **l** 21 **m** 8

13 **a** 7 **b** $4\frac{1}{2}$ **c** 6 **d** $9\frac{1}{2}$ **e** 12 **f** 1 **g** $15\frac{1}{2}$ **h** 10
   i −2 **j** 8

14 **a** $3x°, 2x°$ **b** $x = 30°$ **c** 90°, 60°

15 **a** $(x − 10)°, (x + 40)°$ **b** $x = 50°$ **c** 40°, 90°

16 **a** $x + 20, 2x$ **b** $x = 15°$ **c** 35, 30 pence

17 **a** $x = 7$ **b** £21, £13

18 **a** $x = 686$ **b** 829, 942

19 $x = 21$

20 $x = 2$

21 $x = 14$

22 $y = 13$

23 $z = 12$; 48 years, 41 years

24 $x = 40$

25 $x = 5$

26 $y = 3$

27 $z = 6$

28 $x = 40$

29 $z = 9$; £45, £34

30 $y = 12$; 27 min, 7 min

31 $x = 255$; 380 pages, 221 pages

32 $x = 165$; 200 m², 153 m²

33 12 white, 26 red, 6 black

34 90 kg, 70 kg, 45 kg

35 **a** 2 **b** 4 **c** 12 **d** $6\frac{1}{2}$
   e 4 **f** 6 **g** 4 **h** 5
   i 10 **j** $1\frac{1}{2}$ **k** 1 **l** $2\frac{1}{2}$

Forming equations

Part 2

1 £12, £18

2 £188, £312

3 $x = 36$; 36 years, 33 years, 3 years

4 $x = 34$

5 $z = 21$

6 $x = 8$

7 $y = 9$

8 $x = 45$

9 $x = 40$

10 $z = 12$

11 $x = 15$

12 29 men, 46 women, 76 children

13 $x = 4$

14 $x = 3$

15 **a** $n + 1$
    b $n = 14$

16 **a** $m + 1$
    b $m = 31$

17 **a** $p + 1, p + 2$
    b $p = 32$

18 **a** $q - 1$
    b $q = 25$

19 **a** $r - 1, r - 2$
    b $r = 24$

20 $x = 10$

21 $y = 6$

22 $z = 24$

'3 $x = 5$

24 $x = 4$

25 $y = 5$

26 4 fifty-pence coins
    12 ten-pence coins

27 2 cows, 4 sheep

28 7 hyacinths, 28 crocus

29 **a** $27 - x$
    b $x = 9$

30 **a** $150 - y$
    b $y = 30$

31 **a** $30 - z$
    b $z = 17$

32 **a** $960 - x$
    b $x = 504$

33 **a** $12 - x$
    b $x = 4$

34 **a** $5 - y$
    b $y = 3$

35 **a** $20 - x$
    b 6 10p stamps
      14 15p stamps

36 **a** $24 - x$
    b 20 daffodils and 4 tulips

37 $x = 4$

38 **a** 5   **b** 3   **c** 6   **d** 5

39 **a** 2   **b** $\frac{1}{2}$ **c** $\frac{1}{4}$

40 **a** 6   **b** 3   **c** 7   **d** $3\frac{1}{2}$

41 **a** 2   **b** $2\frac{1}{4}$ **c** 2   **d** $2\frac{1}{3}$
    e 6   **f** $7\frac{1}{2}$ **g** 5

42 $x = 160$

43 $x = 1$

44 $x = 11$

45 $x = 4$

46 $x = 3$

Equations with fractions

Part 1

1	6	9	$\frac{1}{2}$	17	8	25	$2\frac{1}{2}$
2	10	10	$\frac{1}{2}$	18	10	26	$\frac{4}{5}$
3	24	11	$\frac{1}{3}$	19	$1\frac{1}{2}$	27	$1\frac{1}{2}$
4	24	12	$\frac{1}{4}$	20	4	28	$6\frac{3}{4}$
5	18	13	$\frac{1}{4}$	21	12	29	3
6	16	14	6	22	10	30	0
7	3	15	10	23	12		
8	2	16	10	24	$4\frac{1}{2}$		

Part 2

1	16	9	45	17	5	25	15
2	4	10	38	18	2	26	$10\frac{1}{2}$
3	9	11	15	19	8	27	14
4	30	12	21	20	6	28	$2\frac{2}{5}$
5	32	13	28	21	15	29	-5
6	7	14	18	22	8	30	$-1\frac{2}{3}$
7	30	15	54	23	8		
8	6	16	3	24	12		

Part 3

1	1	9	7	17	$1\frac{1}{2}$	25	5
2	3	10	9	18	$5\frac{1}{5}$	26	9
3	4	11	22	19	5	27	8
4	14	12	$2\frac{1}{2}$	20	8	28	1
5	28	13	8	21	$14\frac{1}{2}$	29	$6\frac{1}{2}$
6	19	14	5	22	14	30	$1\frac{1}{2}$
7	7	15	7	23	$8\frac{1}{2}$	31	$2\frac{3}{4}$
8	18	16	5	24	2	32	$5\frac{1}{9}$

Part 4

1	2	9	$4\frac{1}{4}$	17	15	25	$17\frac{1}{2}$
2	5	10	$\frac{1}{2}$	18	24	26	$1\frac{1}{2}$
3	3	11	$\frac{1}{2}$	19	6	27	$3\frac{3}{4}$
4	$3\frac{1}{2}$	12	$\frac{1}{3}$	20	8	28	$1\frac{1}{3}$

Equations with fractions

5	$4\frac{1}{2}$	**13**	$\frac{1}{4}$	**21**	10	**29**	$2\frac{2}{5}$
6	$1\frac{1}{4}$	**14**	$\frac{3}{7}$	**22**	12	**30**	$\frac{1}{9}$
7	$3\frac{1}{3}$	**15**	$\frac{4}{5}$	**23**	$4\frac{1}{2}$	**31**	$\frac{7}{10}$
8	$2\frac{2}{5}$	**16**	6	**24**	$5\frac{1}{3}$	**32**	6

Part 5

1	$7\frac{1}{3}$	**10**	$4\frac{1}{8}$	**19**	$4\frac{4}{5}$	**28**	$-16\frac{1}{2}$
2	$12\frac{1}{2}$	**11**	$3\frac{1}{9}$	**20**	$4\frac{4}{9}$	**29**	$1\frac{2}{5}$
3	$6\frac{2}{3}$	**12**	$5\frac{1}{10}$	**21**	$2\frac{2}{3}$	**30**	-12
4	$3\frac{1}{2}$	**13**	$1\frac{1}{4}$	**22**	$1\frac{1}{5}$	**31**	3
5	$7\frac{1}{2}$	**14**	$2\frac{1}{4}$	**23**	$4\frac{2}{7}$	**32**	-16
6	$7\frac{1}{5}$	**15**	$\frac{2}{9}$	**24**	10	**33**	$\frac{1}{5}$
7	$6\frac{3}{5}$	**16**	$4\frac{4}{9}$	**25**	$-1\frac{1}{7}$	**34**	4
8	$8\frac{1}{4}$	**17**	12	**26**	$-2\frac{6}{7}$	**35**	$3\frac{3}{4}$
9	$2\frac{6}{7}$	**18**	30	**27**	$-4\frac{2}{7}$	**36**	$1\frac{5}{7}$

Part 6

1	**a**	120°	**b**	72°	**c**	90°	**d**	60°	**e**	80°	**f**	60°
	g	75°	**h**	120°	**i**	60°	**j**	80°	**k**	40°	**l**	40°
	m	100°	**n**	60°	**o**	60°	**p**	60°	**q**	40°	**r**	75°
	s	160°	**t**	112°								

2	12	**3**	8	**4**	33	**5**	24	**6**	36	**7**	20		
8	12	**9**	20	**10**	16	**11**	16	**12**	24	**13**	35		
14	10 hours	**15**	3	**16**	8	**17**	20	**18**	12	**19**	16		
20	10 litres	**21**	15 litres	**22**	12	**23**	12	**24**	120 kg	**25**	100 kg		

Part 7

Familiarity with the multiplication of directed numbers will be needed for the equations in parts 3 and 4.

1	**a**	3	**b**	1	**c**	0	**d**	-1	**e**	6	**f**	$\frac{1}{2}$
	g	$\frac{1}{4}$	**h**	-4	**i**	2	**j**	-2	**k**	$\frac{1}{3}$	**l**	$1\frac{4}{5}$
2	**a**	1	**b**	2	**c**	0	**d**	$\frac{1}{2}$	**e**	-1	**f**	-2
	g	12	**h**	10	**i**	6	**j**	-2	**k**	0	**l**	5
3	**a**	2	**b**	2	**c**	4	**d**	-3	**e**	7	**f**	4
	g	-1	**h**	9	**i**	$5\frac{1}{7}$	**j**	7	**k**	$10\frac{2}{5}$	**l**	4
4	**a**	5	**b**	2	**c**	-1	**d**	8	**e**	4	**f**	8
	g	12	**h**	2	**i**	8	**j**	-7				

Simultaneous Equations

Simultaneous equations

Introduction

7 b		**8** b		**9** c		**10** a		**11** b		**12** c
13 b		**14** a		**15** b		**16** a		**17** c		**18** c

The method of elimination

Part 1

1 $x = 1$
$y = 2$

7 $x = 2$
$y = \frac{1}{3}$

13 $x = 1$
$y = -2$

2 $x = 2$
$y = 3$

8 $x = 1$
$y = -1$

14 $x = 2$
$y = 6$

3 $x = 4$
$y = 1$

9 $x = 2$
$y = -1$

15 $x = 4$
$y = -1$

4 $x = 1$
$y = 0$

10 $x = 1$
$y = 3$

16 $x = \frac{1}{2}$
$y = -\frac{1}{3}$

5 $x = 3$
$y = 1$

11 $x = -2$
$y = 5$

17 $x = \frac{2}{3}$
$y = -\frac{5}{6}$

6 $x = 1$
$y = \frac{1}{2}$

12 $x = -\frac{1}{2}$
$y = 4$

18 $x = \frac{3}{4}$
$y = 0$

Part 2

1 $x = 1$
$y = 1$

7 $x = 2$
$y = -1$

13 $x = -1$
$y = 3$

2 $x = 2$
$y = 1$

8 $x = 2$
$y = -\frac{1}{2}$

14 $x = 1$
$y = -3$

3 $x = 3$
$y = 2$

9 $x = 1$
$y = -3$

15 $x = 1$
$y = -4$

4 $x = 8$
$y = 0$

10 $x = 3$
$y = 1$

16 $x = \frac{1}{10}$
$y = -1$

5 $x = \frac{1}{2}$
$y = 1$

11 $x = -2$
$y = 2$

17 $x = -\frac{1}{2}$
$y = 0$

6 $x = \frac{1}{3}$
$y = \frac{1}{2}$

12 $x = 0$
$y = 3$

18 $x = 2$
$y = -\frac{1}{3}$

The method of elimination

Part 3

1 $x = 1$
$y = 2$

2 $x = 2$
$y = 3$

3 $x = 4$
$y = 0$

4 $x = 3$
$y = \frac{1}{2}$

5 $x = 7$
$y = 1$

6 $x = 2$
$y = 0$

7 $x = \frac{1}{2}$
$y = \frac{2}{3}$

8 $x = 1$
$y = 1$

9 $x = 3$
$y = -1$

10 $x = 2$
$y = -2$

11 $x = 9$
$y = 1$

12 $x = 6$
$y = 2$

13 $x = 2$
$y = 1$

14 $x = -1\frac{1}{2}$
$y = -3$

15 $x = 0$
$y = -\frac{1}{4}$

16 $x = -1$
$y = -4$

17 $x = 2$
$y = -\frac{1}{2}$

18 $x = \frac{3}{10}$
$y = -\frac{1}{4}$

Part 4

1 $x = 2$
$y = 1$

2 $x = \frac{2}{3}$
$y = 3\frac{2}{3}$

3 $x = \frac{1}{2}$
$y = \frac{1}{2}$

4 $x = 2$
$y = 0$

5 $x = 1$
$y = 1$

6 $x = 1$
$y = \frac{1}{2}$

7 $x = 3$
$y = \frac{1}{4}$

8 $x = \frac{1}{3}$
$y = 0$

9 $x = 2$
$y = 1$

10 $x = 2$
$y = 7$

11 $x = 4$
$y = 1$

12 $x = 1$
$y = -2$

13 $x = 1$
$y = -2$

14 $x = -2$
$y = 9$

15 $x = -1$
$y = 2$

16 $x = 0$
$y = 0$

17 $x = -1$
$y = 2$

18 $x = -2$
$y = 4$

19 $x = -1$
$y = -1$

20 $x = 1$
$y = -2$

21 $x = 0$
$y = 2$

22 $x = 2$
$y = 1$

23 $x = 1$
$y = 2$

24 $x = 0$
$y = -4$

25 $x = \frac{1}{2}$
$y = -1$

26 $x = \frac{1}{2}$
$y = -\frac{1}{2}$

The method of elimination

Part 5

1	$x = 3$ $y = 2$	**7**	$x = 1$ $y = 3$	**13**	$x = 12$ $y = -1$
2	$x = 5$ $y = 1$	**8**	$x = 2$ $y = \frac{1}{2}$	**14**	$x = 0$ $y = -1$
3	$x = 4$ $y = 2$	**9**	$x = 1$ $y = 1$	**15**	$x = \frac{1}{3}$ $y = -\frac{1}{2}$
4	$x = 3$ $y = 1$	**10**	$x = 3$ $y = 1$	**16**	$x = 3$ $y = -1$
5	$x = 2$ $y = 0$	**11**	$x = 3$ $y = -3$	**17**	$x = 1$ $y = \frac{1}{2}$
6	$x = 2$ $y = \frac{1}{2}$	**12**	$x = 2$ $y = -2$	**18**	$x = 6$ $y = -1$

Part 6

1	$x = 2$ $y = 1$	**7**	$x = 3$ $y = -1$	**13**	$x = 1$ $y = 1$
2	$x = 1$ $y = 3$	**8**	$x = 1$ $y = -2$	**14**	$x = 4$ $y = 4$
3	$x = 3$ $y = \frac{1}{2}$	**9**	$x = 4$ $y = 1$	**15**	$x = 5$ $y = -1$
4	$x = \frac{1}{2}$ $y = 1$	**10**	$x = 1$ $y = \frac{1}{3}$	**16**	$x = \frac{1}{3}$ $y = -\frac{1}{2}$
5	$x = 1$ $y = 1$	**11**	$x = 0$ $y = -3$	**17**	$x = 1$ $y = -1$
6	$x = 3$ $y = -3$	**12**	$x = 1$ $y = 1$	**18**	$x = 3$ $y = \frac{1}{2}$

Part 7

1	$x = 2, y = 3$	**7**	$x = 1, y = \frac{1}{2}$	**13**	$x = 3, y = 4$
2	$x = 5, y = 4$	**8**	$x = -\frac{1}{2}, y = 2$	**14**	$x = 4, y = 1$
3	$x = \frac{1}{5}, y = \frac{1}{4}$	**9**	$x = 1, y = \frac{1}{3}$	**15**	$x = 5, y = 4$
4	$x = 2, y = 5$	**10**	$x = 0, y = -1$	**16**	$x = 1\frac{1}{2}, y = 5$
5	$x = -1, y = 6$	**11**	$x = \frac{1}{2}, y = 0$	**17**	$x = 12, y = 20$
6	$x = 0, y = 4$	**12**	$x = -1, y = -3$	**18**	$x = 20, y = 12$

The method of substitution

Part 1

1 $x = 3$
$y = 10$

6 $x = 6$
$y = 11$

11 $x = 2\frac{1}{2}$
$y = -7$

16 $x = 0$
$y = 8$

2 $x = 3$
$y = 16$

7 $x = 6$
$y = 2$

12 $x = 1\frac{2}{3}$
$y = 5\frac{1}{3}$

17 $x = 3$
$y = -1$

3 $x = 2$
$y = 14$

8 $x = 2$
$y = 8$

13 $x = -1\frac{1}{5}$
$y = 10\frac{2}{5}$

18 $x = \frac{1}{2}$
$y = 2\frac{1}{2}$

4 $x = -2$
$y = -3$

9 $x = 1$
$y = 4$

14 $x = -1\frac{1}{4}$
$y = 7\frac{3}{4}$

5 $x = -6$
$y = -9$

10 $x = 3\frac{1}{3}$
$y = -\frac{2}{3}$

15 $x = 0$
$y = 6$

Part 2

1 $x = 3$
$y = 11$

6 $x = 2$
$y = 1$

11 $x = 5$
$y = 11$

16 $x = -3$
$y = -7$

2 $x = 2$
$y = 5$

7 $x = 3\frac{1}{3}$
$y = 5\frac{1}{3}$

12 $x = -1$
$y = 6$

17 $x = 4\frac{1}{2}$
$y = 3\frac{1}{2}$

3 $x = 2$
$y = 0$

8 $x = 2\frac{1}{8}$
$y = -\frac{3}{8}$

13 $x = -3\frac{1}{2}$
$y = 17$

18 $x = -2\frac{1}{2}$
$y = -2\frac{1}{2}$

4 $x = 1$
$y = 1$

9 $x = \frac{1}{2}$
$y = 8\frac{1}{2}$

14 $x = 2$
$y = -3$

5 $x = 2$
$y = 7$

10 $x = 3$
$y = -1$

15 $x = 3$
$y = 1$

Part 3

1 $x = 7$
$y = 5$

9 $x = 1\frac{1}{5}$
$y = \frac{2}{5}$

17 $x = -13$
$y = -9$

25 $x = -9$
$y = -6\frac{1}{2}$

2 $x = 1$
$y = 4$

10 $x = 0$
$y = 1$

18 $x = 3$
$y = 3$

26 $x = -10$
$y = 5\frac{1}{3}$

3 $x = -3\frac{1}{2}$
$y = -1\frac{1}{2}$

11 $x = -1$
$y = 10$

19 $x = 8$
$y = 2$

27 $x = \frac{4}{25}$
$y = 1\frac{4}{5}$

4 $x = -3$
$y = -5$

12 $x = 5$
$y = 0$

20 $x = 7$
$y = 2$

28 $x = -2\frac{3}{4}$
$y = -3\frac{1}{2}$

The method of substitution

5 $x = 4$
$y = 1$

6 $x = 7$
$y = -1$

7 $x = 2$
$y = 0$

8 $x = 0$
$y = -\frac{1}{2}$

13 $x = 2$
$y = 2$

14 $x = 2$
$y = 1$

15 $x = 2$
$y = 5$

16 $x = 1$
$y = 2$

21 $x = 1$
$y = 1$

22 $x = 15$
$y = 37$

23 $x = 1\frac{1}{2}$
$y = \frac{1}{2}$

24 $x = 1\frac{1}{2}$
$y = 5\frac{1}{2}$

29 $x = 0$
$y = 0$

30 $x = 6$
$y = 0$

The matrix method

1 $x = 1$
$y = 3$

2 $x = 2$
$y = 1$

3 $x = 2$
$y = -1$

4 $x = 1$
$y = -1$

5 $x = 0$
$y = -2$

6 $x = 1$
$y = \frac{1}{2}$

7 $x = 26$
$y = 17$

8 $x = -\frac{1}{2}$
$y = 0$

9 $x = 1$
$y = \frac{1}{2}$

10 $x = -4$
$y = 8$

11 $x = 3$
$y = \frac{1}{4}$

12 $x = 5$
$y = -2$

13 $x = 1\frac{1}{2}$
$y = 0$

14 $x = 3$
$y = -1$

15 $x = 1$
$y = -\frac{1}{3}$

16 $x = -1$
$y = -2$

17 $x = 0$
$y = -3$

18 $x = 1$
$y = -6$

19 $x = 1$
$y = 1$

20 $x = 8$
$y = -6$

21 $x = 3$
$y = 0$

22 $x = 1$
$y = \frac{1}{2}$

23 $x = 2$
$y = -1$

24 $x = \frac{1}{2}$
$y = \frac{1}{3}$

25 $x = -2\frac{1}{5}$
$y = -2\frac{4}{5}$

26 $x = \frac{2}{3}$
$y = -1$

27 $x = 1\frac{1}{2}$
$y = 0$

28 $x = 2$
$y = 1$

29 $x = 5$
$y = 2$

30 $x = \frac{1}{4}$
$y = \frac{1}{2}$

31 $x = -3$
$y = -1$

32 $x = -2\frac{1}{2}$
$y = 5$

33 $x = 1$
$y = 1$

34 $x = -\frac{1}{2}$
$y = 4$

35 $x = 0$
$y = 1\frac{1}{2}$

36 $x = 8$
$y = -\frac{1}{2}$

37 $x = 2$
$y = 5$

38 $x = \frac{1}{2}$
$y = 1$

39 $x = 1$
$y = \frac{1}{2}$

40 $x = -1$
$y = 1$

Graphical methods

Introduction

1 $x = 3$
$y = 5$

2 $x = 2$
$y = 5$

3 $x = 4$
$y = 5$

4 $x = 2$
$y = 3$

5 $x = 0$
$y = 3$

6 $x = 2\frac{1}{2}$
$y = 1$

7 $x = 2$
$y = 3$

8 $x = 2$
$y = 3$

Part 1 Point by point

1 $x = 2$
$y = 5$

2 $x = 4$
$y = 6$

3 $x = 1\frac{1}{2}$
$y = 2$

4 $x = 1$
$y = 3\frac{1}{2}$

5 $x = 2\frac{1}{2}$
$y = 3\frac{1}{2}$

6 $x = 4\frac{1}{2}$
$y = 3\frac{1}{2}$

7 $x = -2$
$y = 3$

8 $x = 2\frac{1}{2}$
$y = 5\frac{1}{2}$

9 $x = -1$
$y = 5\frac{1}{2}$

10 $x = 5$
$y = 1\frac{1}{3}$

Part 2 The gradient and y-intercept method

1 $x = 3$
$y = 5$

2 $x = 2$
$y = 4$

3 $x = -2$
$y = -3$

4 $x = 4$
$y = 6$

5 $x = -3$
$y = -6$

6 $x = 6$
$y = 4$

7 $x = -2$
$y = -1$

8 $x = -1$
$y = 1$

9 $x = 3$
$y = 2$

10 $x = 3$
$y = -1$

11 $x = 2$
$y = 0$

12 $x = 2$
$y = -1$

13 $x = 3$
$y = 7$

14 $x = 3$
$y = 6$

15 $x = 4$
$y = -2$

16 $x = 2$
$y = 0$

17 $x = 1$
$y = -2$

18 $x = -4$
$y = -5$

19 $x = -1$
$y = 0$

20 $x = 2$
$y = 5$

21 $x = 6$
$y = 4$

22 $x = -3$
$y = -2\frac{1}{2}$

23 $x = 3$
$y = 5\frac{1}{2}$

24 $x = 1$
$y = \frac{1}{2}$

25 $x = -2$
$y = 0$

26 $x = -1\frac{1}{2}$
$y = -1\frac{3}{4}$

27 $x = 4$
$y = 0$

28 $x = -4$
$y = 3$

Part 3 Using both intercepts

1 $x = 3$
$y = 2$

2 $x = 3$
$y = 2$

3 $x = 3$
$y = 4$

4 $x = 3$
$y = 1\frac{1}{2}$

5 $x = 6$
$y = 2$

6 $x = 2$
$y = 2$

7 $x = 4$
$y = 5$

8 $x = 2$
$y = -1\frac{1}{2}$

9 $x = -1\frac{1}{2}$
$y = 4$

10 $x = 2$
$y = 3$

11 $x = -2$
$y = -1$

12 $x = 3$
$y = -1$

13 $x = 6$
$y = 4$

14 $x = 3$
$y = -2$

15 $x = -2$
$y = 1$

16 $x = -2\frac{1}{2}$
$y = -1$

Graphical methods

Part 4 A mixture

1 $x = 2$ $y = 5$	**2** $x = 2$ $y = 5$	**3** $x = 2$ $y = 2$	**4** No solutions
5 No solutions	**6** Infinite solutions	**7** $x = 2$ $y = 0$	**8** $x = 2$ $y = 3$
9 Infinite solutions	**10** Infinite solutions	**11** $x = 0$ $y = 6$	**12** Infinite solutions
13 No solutions	**14** $x = 3$ $y = 0$	**15** Infinite solutions	**16** No solutions

Problems involving simultaneous equations

1 $x = 25$ $y = 14$	**2** $p = 18$ $q = 9$	**3** 36 pence 30 pence	**4** 47 pence 29 pence
5 $c = 20$ $i = 10$	**6** $c = 3$ $r = 4$	**7** £6 per adult £4 per child	**8** $c = 120$ $s = 50$
9 50 grams 25 grams	**10** $d = 30$ $c = 25$	**11** $\frac{1}{2}$ m $\frac{1}{4}$ m	**12** 30 pence 20 pence
13 45 pence 30 pence	**14** 2 m $\frac{1}{2}$ m	**15** a $x = 5$ cm $y = 2$ cm b $x = 8$ cm $y = 4$ cm c $x = 2$ cm $y = 4$ cm	

16 a $x = 9$ b $x = 10$ c $x = 4$
      $y = 3$ $y = 2$ $y = 4$

17 a $x = 36°$ b $x = 45°$ c $x = 50°$
      $y = 72°$ $y = 15°$ $y = 40°$

18 $x = 72°$ **19** $x = 3$ **20** $x = 53$ **21** $x = 13288$
    $y = 36°$ $y = \frac{3}{4}$ $y = 29$ $y = 13052$

22 b   45 years   **23** b   25 years   **24** 60 years   **25** 43 oranges
      15 years   5 years   5 years   4 children

26 32 apples
    5 children

Expansions and Factors

Expansions and factors

$x(x + 2)$ can be expressed visually as the area of a rectangle of width x and length $x + 2$.
The same area can also be expressed as the sum of the two areas x^2 and $2x$.
Hence we can write $x(x + 2) = x^2 + 2x$.

A similar visual representation of $(x + 2)(x + 3)$ can be given to provide the total area of the rectangle of width $x + 2$ and length $x + 3$.
Hence $(x + 2)(x + 3) = x^2 + 3x + 2x + 6$
$$= x^2 \quad + 5x \quad + 6.$$

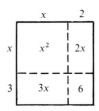

Some teachers might also find "thought lines" useful to emphasise the multiplications involved, for example

$x(x + 2) = x^2 + 2x$ and $(x + 2)(x + 3) = x^2 + 3x + 2x + 6$.

1 **a** $x^2 + 2x$ **b** $x^2 + 4x$
    c $x^2 + 5x$ **d** $3x + 12$
    e $2x + 12$ **f** $4x + 8$

2
a $x^2 - 2x$	**h** $15x + 12$	**o** $3x^2 + 21x$
b $x^2 - 4x$	**i** $12x - 8$	**p** $4x^2 - 12x$
c $x^2 + 9x$	**j** $16x - 40$	**q** $8x^2 - 40x$
d $x^2 + 12x$	**k** $4x^2 - 3x$	**r** $16x^2 - 40x$
e $3x + 18$	**l** $3x^2 - 7x$	**s** $9x^2 + 12x$
f $4x + 20$	**m** $5x^2 + 6x$	**t** $10x^2 - 6x$
g $4x + 6$	**n** $5x^2 + 30x$	**u** $8x^2 + 4x$

3
a $x^3 + 3x^2 + 4x$	**i** $12x^2 + 16x - 28$
b $x^3 - 5x^2 + 2x$	**j** $12x^3 - 18x^2 + 3x$
c $x^3 + 6x^2 - 7x$	**k** $6x^3 + 12x^2 + 8x$
d $2x^3 - 4x^2 + 3x$	**l** $8x^3 + 4x^2 + 12x$
e $3x^3 + 4x^2 - 5x$	**m** $12x^3 - 3x^2 - 3x$
f $2x^2 - 6x - 8$	**n** $24x^3 - 48x^2 + 8x$
g $3x^2 + 18x - 15$	**o** $40x^2 - 8x + 16$
h $12x^2 - 12x + 18$	**p** $9x^4 + 6x^3 - 21x^2$

4
a $14x + 9$	**h** $7x - 18$	**o** $2x^2 + 4x$	**u** $4x^2 + 3x$
b $27x + 4$	**i** $20x - 17$	**p** $2x^2 + 3x$	**v** $2x^2 + 21x$
c $10x + 8$	**j** $2x + 8$	**q** $2x^2 - 8x$	**w** $2x^2 - 16x$
d $9x - 4$	**k** $2x + 2$	**r** $2x^2 - 2x$	**x** $14x^2 + 3x$
e $17x - 8$	**l** $9x - 1$	**s** $5x^2 + 7x$	**y** $3x^2$
f $10x + 3$	**m** $7x + 3$	**t** $6x^2 + 2x$	**z** 0
g $12x - 4$	**n** $2x^2 + 7x$		

Expansions and factors

5
- **a** $2x^3 + 9x^2 + 9x$
- **b** $2x^3 + 3x^2 - 2x$
- **c** $2x^2 + 3x$
- **d** $4x^2 + 4x$
- **e** $2x^3 - 4x^2 + 2x$
- **f** $x^2 - 2x$
- **g** $5x^3 + 3x$
- **h** $5x^3 + 9x^2 + 4x$

- **i** $2x^3 - 6x^2$
- **j** $12x^3 - x^2 + 18x - 10$
- **k** $14x^3 + 3x^2 - 3$
- **l** $6x^3 - 12x^2 + 13x - 8$
- **m** $5x^3 + 11x^2 - 25x$
- **n** $22x$
- **o** 0
- **p** $5x^4 - 5x^3 + 4x$

6
- **a** $xy + 3x$
- **b** $2xy + 8x$
- **c** $12xy + 15x$
- **d** $14xy - 21x$
- **e** $15xy - 10xz$
- **f** $10xy + 8xz$
- **g** $x^2 + 2xy$
- **h** $3x^2 - 12xy$

- **i** $5x^2 - 15xy + 10xz$
- **j** $5xy + 4x$
- **k** $6xy + 4x$
- **l** $5xy - 17x$
- **m** $xy - 6xz$
- **n** $17xy + 2xz$
- **o** $3xy$
- **p** $12x^2 - 4xy$

- **q** $-3xy$
- **r** $3x^2$
- **s** $8x^2 + 3xy$
- **t** $8x^2 - 4xy + 7x$
- **u** $x^2 + 3xy - 7x$
- **v** $x^2 - 13xy + 9x$
- **w** $4xy + y^2 + y$
- **x** $7xy + 7y^2 - 15y$

Common factors

Part 1

1	$2(x + 4)$	**10**	$x(5y + 7)$	**19**	$6z(3z - 2y)$		
2	$3(x + 3)$	**11**	$3x(y + 2)$	**20**	$3y(3y - 1)$		
3	$5(x - 4)$	**12**	$4x(y - 2)$	**21**	$5z(1 + 2z)$		
4	$3(2x + 3)$	**13**	$5z(y + 2)$	**22**	$pq(6 - 5pq)$		
5	$2(2x - 5)$	**14**	$2z(2y + 3)$	**23**	$4ab(2 + ab)$		
6	$3(3x + 5)$	**15**	$2x(4x + 5)$	**24**	$x(2x^3 - 3)$		
7	$x(y + 3)$	**16**	$3x(3x - 4)$	**25**	$4x(x^3 + 3)$		
8	$x(y - 5)$	**17**	$3x(2y - 3x)$	**26**	$xy(5x - y)$		
9	$x(2y - 3)$	**18**	$2x(4z + 3x)$				

Part 2

1	$3(x + 4)$	**10**	$y(5y + 7)$	**19**	$xy(xy - 6)$		
2	$3(2x + 5)$	**11**	$5y(y + 3)$	**20**	$x(y - 4x)$		
3	$4(2z - 5)$	**12**	$3p(p - 3)$	**21**	$y(x + 5y)$		
4	$3(2z + 1)$	**13**	$4p(2p + 1)$	**22**	$2xy(xy + 3)$		
5	$5(2y + 1)$	**14**	$x(x^2 + 7x + 4)$	**23**	$x(x^2 + xy + y^2)$		
6	$y(x + 7)$	**15**	$2x(x^2 - 3x + 4)$	**24**	$2x(x^2 - 4x + 1)$		
7	$z(x - 4)$	**16**	$5y(y^2 + 2y - 4)$	**25**	$xy(x^2y^2 - xy + 1)$		
8	$2x(y - 3)$	**17**	$y^2(y + 1)$	**26**	$3pq(5p - q)$		
9	$x(x - 6)$	**18**	$2x^2(x - 2)$				

34

Common factors

Part 3

1	50	8	80	15	84	22	24
2	560	9	130	16	23000	23	28
3	140	10	42	17	740	24	189.2
4	190	11	34	18	560	25	15.7
5	50	12	8600	19	72	26	125.6
6	34	13	370	20	130		
7	120	14	32	21	120		

More expansions

Part 1

1 $x^2 + 5x + 6$ 3 $x^2 + 10x + 24$

2 $x^2 + 6x + 5$ 4 $x^2 + 8x + 15$

Part 2

1	$x^2 + 9x + 20$	10	$x^2 - 6x - 40$	19	$x^2 - 6x + 9$
2	$x^2 + 10x + 21$	11	$x^2 - 2x - 63$	20	$x^2 - 7x + 10$
3	$x^2 + 13x + 40$	12	$x^2 - 9x + 18$	21	$x^2 - 16$
4	$x^2 + 11x + 28$	13	$x^2 - 6x + 8$	22	$x^2 + 3x - 18$
5	$x^2 + 2x - 8$	14	$x^2 - 15x + 56$	23	$x^2 - 81$
6	$x^2 + 5x - 24$	15	$x^2 - 3x - 10$	24	$x^2 + 4x - 21$
7	$x^2 + 7x - 18$	16	$x^2 - 9$	25	$x^2 + 6x + 9$
8	$x^2 + 4x - 21$	17	$x^2 + 8x + 16$	26	$x^2 - 7x - 18$
9	$x^2 - 2x - 8$	18	$x^2 + 12x + 36$		

Part 3

1	$6x^2 + 19x + 15$	7	$16x^2 + 2x - 3$	13	$4x^2 - 20x + 25$
2	$8x^2 + 14x + 5$	8	$10x^2 - 11x - 6$	14	$9x^2 + 24x + 16$
3	$10x^2 + 19x + 6$	9	$12x^2 - 7x - 10$	15	$9x^2 - 16$
4	$24x^2 + 38x + 8$	10	$3x^2 - 10x - 8$	16	$49x^2 - 4$
5	$6x^2 + 7x - 20$	11	$4x^2 - 25$		
6	$9x^2 + 6x - 35$	12	$4x^2 + 20x + 25$		

Part 4

1	$x^2 + 3xy + 2y^2$	7	$6x^2 + xy - y^2$	13	$16x^2 + 46xy + 15y^2$
2	$x^2 + 5xy + 6y^2$	8	$48x^2 + 2xy - y^2$	14	$6x^2 + 13xy - 28y^2$
3	$x^2 + 9xy + 20y^2$	9	$6x^2 - xy - y^2$	15	$2x^2 + 11xy - 40y^2$
4	$x^2 + 10xy + 21y^2$	10	$16x^2 - y^2$	16	$4x^2 - 12xy + 9y^2$
5	$6x^2 + 5xy + y^2$	11	$9x^2 + 12xy + 4y^2$	17	$10x^2 - 24xy + 8y^2$
6	$20x^2 + 9xy + y^2$	12	$8x^2 + 14xy + 5y^2$	18	$16x^2 - 24xy + 9y^2$

The difference of two squares

Part 1

1 $x^2 - 4$

2 $x^2 - 9$

3 $4x^2 - 25$

4 $9x^2 - 16$

5 $x^2 - y^2$

6 $4x^2 - 9y^2$

7 $(x - 5)(x + 5)$

8 $(x - 6)(x + 6)$

9 $(x - 10)(x + 10)$

10 $(x - 1)(x + 1)$

11 $(3x - 2)(3x + 2)$

12 $(4x - 3)(4x + 3)$

13 $(2x - y)(2x + y)$

14 $(3x - 2y)(3x + 2y)$

15 $(6x - 5y)(6x + 5y)$

16 $(10x - 3y)(10x + 3y)$

17 $(7a - b)(7a + b)$

18 $(\frac{1}{2}a - 2b)(\frac{1}{2}a + 2b)$

19 $(\frac{1}{4}p - 4q)(\frac{1}{4}p + 4q)$

20 $(p - \frac{1}{3}q)(p + \frac{1}{3}q)$

21 $(mn - 3)(mn + 3)$

22 $(\frac{1}{2}x - 4)(\frac{1}{2}x + 4)$

23 $(xy - \frac{1}{2}z)(xy + \frac{1}{2}z)$

24 $(a^2 - 3)(a^2 + 3)$

Part 2

1 9600

2 8200

3 7600

4 10 800

5 11 600

6 998 000

7 982 000

8 640

9 3200

10 572 000

11 180

12 600

13 153

14 685

15 843

16 1 234 200

Part 3

1 3.8

2 16

3 52

4 154

5 7540

6 4360

7 3160

8 14.24

9 260

10 34

11 76

12 15

13 19

14 6

15 10

16 19

Quadratic factors

Part 1

1 $(x + 1)(x + 3)$

2 $(x + 5)(x + 1)$

3 $(x + 2)(x + 4)$

4 $(x + 2)(x + 5)$

5 $(x + 1)(x + 10)$

6 $(x - 10)(x - 1)$

7 $(x + 3)(x + 5)$

8 $(x - 5)(x - 3)$

9 $(x + 2)(x + 10)$

10 $(x - 10)(x - 2)$

11 $(x - 7)(x - 2)$

12 $(x - 6)(x - 5)$

13 $(x - 4)(x - 3)$

14 $(x - 1)(x + 7)$

15 $(x - 7)(x + 1)$

16 $(x - 1)(x + 5)$

17 $(x - 5)(x + 1)$

18 $(x - 2)(x + 4)$

19 $(x - 4)(x + 2)$

20 $(x - 3)(x + 5)$

21 $(x - 5)(x + 3)$

22 $(x - 6)(x + 2)$

23 $(x - 3)(x + 6)$

24 $(x - 2)(x + 12)$

25 $(x - 8)(x + 2)$

26 $(x - 5)(x + 4)$

Quadratic factors

Part 2

1 $(x + 2)(x + 9)$
2 $(x + 3)(x + 7)$
3 $(x - 11)(x - 2)$
4 $(x - 7)(x - 5)$
5 $(x - 3)(x - 3)$
6 $(x - 1)(x + 8)$
7 $(x - 8)(x + 1)$
8 $(x - 5)(x + 7)$
9 $(x - 7)(x + 5)$

10 $(x - 6)(x + 3)$
11 $(x - 2)(x + 9)$
12 $(x - 6)(x + 2)$
13 $(x - 3)(x + 4)$
14 $(x - 2)(x + 8)$
15 $(x - 4)(x - 4)$
16 $(x - 10)(x - 3)$
17 $(x - 15)(x - 2)$
18 $(x + 3)(x + 9)$

19 $(x - 8)(x - 4)$
20 $(x - 8)(x + 7)$
21 $(x - 6)(x + 8)$
22 $(x - 2)(x + 24)$
23 $(x - 16)(x + 3)$
24 $(x - 9)(x + 8)$
25 $(x + 7)(x + 9)$
26 $(x - 9)(x + 16)$

A mixture of factors

Part 1

1 $4(x + 2y)$
2 $3(2x - 3y)$
3 $(x - 4)(x + 4)$
4 $(y - 5)(y + 5)$
5 $(x + 1)(x + 5)$
6 $(x + 1)(x + 7)$
7 $y(x + 6)$
8 $p(q - 4)$
9 $(2x - 3)(2x + 3)$

10 $(y - 5z)(y + 5z)$
11 $(x - 12)(x - 1)$
12 $(x - 6)(x - 7)$
13 $3a(2b - c)$
14 $a(a - 2b)$
15 $3x(x - 2y)$
16 $4x(3 - x)$
17 $(3 - 2x)(3 + 2x)$
18 $(1 - 5y)(1 + 5y)$

19 $(x + 11)(x - 1)$
20 $(x + 9)(x - 5)$
21 $(x - 8)(x + 4)$
22 $(x - 5)(x - 6)$
23 $x^2(x^2 - 3y^2)$
24 $(x^2 + 1)(x^2 - 1)$ or $[(x + 1)(x - 1)]$ $\times [(x + 1)(x - 1)]$
25 $(x^2 + y^2)(x^2 - y^2)$ or $[(x + y)(x - y)]$ $\times [(x + y)(x - y)]$
26 $3x(2x - 1)$

Part 2

1 $x(4 + y)$
2 $x(5 - x)$
3 $(3 - x)(3 + x)$
4 $(x - \frac{1}{2})(x + \frac{1}{2})$
5 $(x - 5)(x + 4)$
6 $(x + 5)(x + 4)$
7 $x(x + 9)$
8 $xy(xy - 3)$
9 $x(x - 1)$

10 $x(x^2 - 1)$
11 $(x - 5)(x - 3)$
12 $(x - 6)^2$
13 $(x - 2)(x + 2)$
14 $x(x - 4)$
15 $(x - 2)^2$
16 $(x - 9)(x + 5)$
17 $(xy + 5)(xy - 5)$
18 $(1 + pq)(1 - pq)$

19 $(\frac{1}{2}p + 3q)(\frac{1}{2}p - 3q)$
20 $3p(p - 1)(p + 1)$
21 $5q(1 - 2q)(1 + 2q)$
22 $(x - 4)(x - 9)$
23 $(p + 5)(p - 4)$
24 $p(p + 8)(p + 1)$
25 $x(x - 3)^2$
26 $2(x - 7)(x - 2)$

Part 3

1	3	4	3	7	-4	10	1	13	1	16	-2
2	5	5	2	8	-9	11	$2\frac{1}{4}$	14	8		
3	4	6	$\frac{1}{2}$	9	$4\frac{1}{2}$	12	5	15	2		

A mixture of factors

Part 4

Some preliminary discussion will be needed to establish that if $ab = 0$ then either $a = 0$ or $b = 0$.

Hence, for example, if $x(x - 5) = 0$ then either $x = 0$ or $x = 5$.

1	0, 5	**7**	0, 7	**13**	0, -3	**19**	0, $-\frac{1}{3}$	**25**	0, $-1\frac{1}{4}$
2	0, 9	**8**	0, -6	**14**	0, -2	**20**	0, $-\frac{2}{3}$	**26**	0, $1\frac{3}{4}$
3	0, 4	**9**	0, -6	**15**	0, 2	**21**	0, $\frac{3}{4}$		
4	0, -4	**10**	0, 2	**16**	0, $\frac{1}{2}$	**22**	0, $\frac{3}{4}$		
5	0, -8	**11**	0, 4	**17**	0, $\frac{1}{2}$	**23**	0, $1\frac{1}{3}$		
6	0, 3	**12**	0, 3	**18**	0, $\frac{1}{3}$	**24**	0, $-1\frac{1}{2}$		

Part 5

1	0, 7	**7**	0, 2	**13**	0, $-\frac{1}{2}$	**19**	0, -6	**25**	0, ± 4
2	0, 8	**8**	0, 3	**14**	0, $\frac{1}{2}$	**20**	0, $\frac{1}{2}$	**26**	0, ± 2
3	0, -2	**9**	0, 2	**15**	0, $\frac{2}{3}$	**21**	0, $\frac{2}{3}$		
4	0, -3	**10**	0, -4	**16**	0, $\frac{2}{3}$	**22**	0, $1\frac{1}{3}$		
5	0, -1	**11**	0, -3	**17**	0, $-1\frac{1}{4}$	**23**	0, $-1\frac{1}{2}$		
6	0, 1	**12**	0, $\frac{1}{2}$	**18**	0, 2	**24**	0, ± 3		

Part 6

1	± 3	**7**	$\pm 1\frac{1}{2}$	**13**	± 1	**19**	$\pm \frac{4}{5}$	**25**	$\pm \frac{1}{3}$
2	± 6	**8**	$\pm 4\frac{1}{2}$	**14**	$\pm \frac{1}{2}$	**20**	$\pm \frac{7}{10}$	**26**	$\pm \frac{1}{4}$
3	± 9	**9**	$\pm 1\frac{1}{3}$	**15**	$\pm \frac{1}{3}$	**21**	$\pm \frac{1}{10}$		
4	± 8	**10**	$\pm 2\frac{1}{3}$	**16**	$\pm \frac{2}{3}$	**22**	± 6		
5	± 12	**11**	$\pm 2\frac{2}{5}$	**17**	$\pm \frac{3}{4}$	**23**	± 4		
6	± 11	**12**	$\pm 1\frac{1}{6}$	**18**	$\pm \frac{1}{4}$	**24**	$\pm \frac{1}{2}$		

Part 7

1	± 2	**7**	$\pm \frac{1}{6}$	**13**	$\pm \frac{1}{5}$	**19**	$\pm \frac{1}{3}$	**25**	$\pm \frac{1}{2}$
2	± 4	**8**	$\pm \frac{5}{6}$	**14**	± 7	**20**	$\pm \frac{1}{10}$	**26**	$\pm 1\frac{1}{2}$
3	± 5	**9**	$\pm 1\frac{1}{6}$	**15**	$\pm 4\frac{1}{2}$	**21**	$\pm \frac{1}{6}$		
4	$\pm 3\frac{1}{2}$	**10**	$\pm 2\frac{1}{2}$	**16**	$\pm \frac{3}{10}$	**22**	± 1		
5	$\pm 3\frac{1}{3}$	**11**	$\pm 2\frac{2}{3}$	**17**	$\pm \frac{2}{5}$	**23**	± 2		
6	$\pm \frac{1}{2}$	**12**	$\pm \frac{2}{3}$	**18**	$\pm \frac{1}{2}$	**24**	± 3		

Part 8

1	$-1, -5$	**3**	$-8, -1$	**5**	$-3, -4$	**7**	2, 6	**9**	2, 5
2	$-1, -7$	**4**	$-2, -4$	**6**	$-2, -6$	**8**	1, 3	**10**	1, -5

A mixture of factors

11 $-1, 5$	**15** $2, -7$	**19** $-3, -6$	**23** $4, -9$	
12 $1, -7$	**16** $2, -8$	**20** $-4, -7$	**24** $-5, -5$	
13 $3, -5$	**17** $5, -4$	**21** $5, 8$	**25** $3, 8$	
14 $5, -3$	**18** $3, -4$	**22** $3, -7$	**26** $-7, -7$	

Part 9

1 $-1, -1\frac{1}{2}$	**7** $3\frac{1}{2}, 1$	**13** $2\frac{1}{2}, -1$	**19** $-\frac{1}{5}, -5$	**25** $\frac{1}{7}, -1$
2 $-1, -2\frac{1}{2}$	**8** $5, 1\frac{1}{2}$	**14** $1, -2\frac{1}{2}$	**20** $-\frac{2}{3}, -1$	**26** $1, -1\frac{2}{5}$
3 $-\frac{1}{2}, -7$	**9** $3, 2\frac{1}{2}$	**15** $2, -\frac{1}{5}$	**21** $\frac{2}{3}, -1$	
4 $-\frac{1}{2}, -2$	**10** $3\frac{1}{2}, 3$	**16** $-\frac{2}{5}, -1$	**22** $\frac{1}{3}, -1$	
5 $-\frac{1}{2}, -5$	**11** $1\frac{1}{2}, -1$	**17** $1, \frac{3}{5}$	**23** $1, -2\frac{1}{3}$	
6 $5\frac{1}{2}, 1$	**12** $1, -1\frac{1}{2}$	**18** $3, \frac{1}{5}$	**24** $1, \frac{1}{7}$	

Part 10

1 $0, 7$	**7** $-1, -7$	**13** $0, -7$	**19** $0, 2\frac{1}{4}$	**25** $-6, 2$
2 $0, -6$	**8** $0, -8$	**14** ± 5	**20** $\pm 1\frac{1}{2}$	**26** $-8, 3$
3 ± 3	**9** $8, 1$	**15** $\pm 2\frac{1}{2}$	**21** $3, -2$	
4 ± 2	**10** $0, 9$	**16** $\pm 1\frac{1}{4}$	**22** $0, 2$	
5 $0, 4$	**11** ± 3	**17** $0, 4$	**23** ± 10	
6 $-1, -5$	**12** $-5, -2$	**18** ± 2	**24** $8, -1$	

Part 11

1 $0, 8$	**7** $-5, -2$	**13** $0, 4$	**19** ± 1	**25** $0, -5, 3$
2 $0, -5$	**8** $0, 6$	**14** ± 2	**20** $0, -2, -7$	**26** $0, 8, -2$
3 ± 3	**9** $5, 1$	**15** ± 3	**21** $0, 3, 5$	
4 $\pm 1\frac{2}{3}$	**10** $0, \pm 3$	**16** $\pm \frac{1}{2}$	**22** $0, 3$	
5 $0, 2$	**11** $0, 1$	**17** $0, -\frac{1}{4}$	**23** ± 1	
6 $-3, -1$	**12** $4, -3$	**18** $0, -6$	**24** $0, 1$	

Part 12

1 $0, -5$	**7** $-2, -9$	**13** $1, -6$	**19** $0, 7$	**25** $-4, 6$
2 $0, -7$	**8** $-4, -5$	**14** ± 3	**20** $0, -7$	**26** $4, 6$
3 $0, 7$	**9** $1, 5$	**15** ± 2	**21** $0, -1$	
4 ± 4	**10** $2, -5$	**16** ± 1	**22** $0, 9$	
5 ± 6	**11** 4	**17** ± 4	**23** ± 5	
6 ± 2	**12** $1, -5$	**18** $0, -3$	**24** $-4, 8$	

Quadratic Equations

Solution by factors

Solution by formula

Solution by graphical methods

Solution by factors

Part 1

1 0, 2	**7** −4, 6	**13** −3	**19** $2\frac{1}{5}, -2\frac{1}{3}$	**25** $-7\frac{1}{2}, -2\frac{2}{3}$
2 0, 7	**8** −3, −2	**14** 7, −6	**20** $-2\frac{1}{2}, -4\frac{1}{2}$	**26** $\frac{3}{4}, -\frac{1}{2}$
3 0, −6	**9** −7, −10	**15** −1, 14	**21** $2\frac{1}{4}, -1\frac{1}{6}$	**27** $\frac{2}{5}$
4 0, −12	**10** 0, −4	**16** $2\frac{1}{2}, 3\frac{1}{2}$	**22** $0, 5\frac{1}{2}$	**28** $1\frac{5}{6}$
5 1, 7	**11** 6	**17** $4\frac{1}{2}, -1\frac{1}{2}$	**23** $0, 3\frac{1}{5}$	**29** $0, -\frac{1}{3}$
6 3, 8	**12** 4	**18** $3\frac{1}{3}, -5\frac{1}{2}$	**24** $0, -2\frac{2}{3}$	**30** $-3\frac{1}{2}, -\frac{2}{3}$

Part 2

1 $x^2 - 5x + 6 = 0$

2 $x^2 - 11x + 30 = 0$

3 $x^2 - 5x + 4 = 0$

4 $x^2 - 7x = 0$

5 $x^2 - x - 6 = 0$

6 $x^2 - 2x - 15 = 0$

7 $x^2 - 16 = 0$

8 $x^2 + 5x - 6 = 0$

9 $x^2 - 5x - 6 = 0$

10 $x^2 + 3x - 28 = 0$

11 $x^2 - 3x - 28 = 0$

12 $x^2 + 5x = 0$

13 $x^2 + 11x + 24 = 0$

14 $x^2 + 14x + 45 = 0$

15 $x^2 + 13x + 30 = 0$

16 $x^2 - 10x = 0$

17 $x^2 + 7x - 30 = 0$

18 $x^2 - 6x + 9 = 0$

19 $x^2 + 6x + 9 = 0$

20 $2x^2 - x = 0$

21 $4x^2 + x = 0$

22 $6x^2 - 5x + 1 = 0$

23 $9x^2 + 12x + 4 = 0$

24 $4x^2 - 3x = 0$

25 $20x^2 - 13x + 2 = 0$

Part 3

1 −1, −3	**11** 2, 2	**21** −1, −18	**31** −1, −12	**41** 8, −6
2 −1, −5	**12** 1, −7	**22** 18, 1	**32** 12, +1	**42** 24, 2
3 −1, −8	**13** 1, −11	**23** 6, 3	**33** 12, −1	**43** 1, −48
4 −2, −4	**14** 15, −1	**24** 3, −6	**34** 3, −4	**44** 3, −16
5 −1, −9	**15** 5, −3	**25** 6, −3	**35** 4, 3	**45** 9, −8
6 −3, −3	**16** 3, −5	**26** 5, 4	**36** −2, −6	**46** 24, 3
7 5, 1	**17** 1, −8	**27** 3, −7	**37** 6, 2	**47** 24, −6
8 14, 1	**18** 8, −1	**28** 8, −4	**38** 2, −6	**48** −9, −16
9 7, 2	**19** −1, −8	**29** 9, 4	**39** 4, −5	
10 4, 1	**20** 8, 1	**30** 18, 2	**40** 10, 2	

Solution by factors

Part 4

1	3, −9	**11**	7, −1	**21**	−4, −6	**31**	3, −4	**41**	9, −3
2	7, −5	**12**	3, −11	**22**	11, 4	**32**	8, 1	**42**	2, 18
3	6, −7	**13**	2, −1	**23**	7, −4	**33**	6, −2	**43**	7, −6
4	8, 3	**14**	12, 3	**24**	32, 2	**34**	9, −3	**44**	4, −6
5	−3, −9	**15**	21, 1	**25**	16,2	**35**	−2, −7	**45**	8, −4
6	9, −5	**16**	9, 6	**26**	2, −13	**36**	−3, −5	**46**	3, −6
7	3, −15	**17**	5, −9	**27**	11, 2	**37**	3, −8	**47**	−5, 10
8	7, −9	**18**	13, −1	**28**	−1, −15	**38**	7, −1	**48**	2, −12
9	−3, −21	**19**	−8, 3	**29**	−2, −5	**39**	11, 3		
10	7, −12	**20**	1, −11	**30**	2, −4	**40**	7, 5		

Part 5

1	±5	**7**	0, 4	**13**	0, −7	**19**	0, 1	**25**	±$2\frac{1}{2}$
2	±2	**8**	±4	**14**	±6	**20**	±9	**26**	±$3\frac{1}{2}$
3	0, 5	**9**	0, 16	**15**	0, −2	**21**	0, 81	**27**	0, 2
4	0, 7	**10**	±7	**16**	±10	**22**	0, −81	**28**	0, −3
5	±3	**11**	0, 8	**17**	0, −3	**23**	±1	**29**	±$1\frac{1}{3}$
6	0, 9	**12**	0, −8	**18**	0, −1	**24**	±$\frac{1}{2}$	**30**	±$1\frac{3}{4}$

Part 6

1 4, −5 **2** 6, −5 **3** 3 cm **4** 2 cm **5** 3 cm **6** 6 cm **7** 4 m

8 8 cm **9** 9 cm **10** 4 cm **11** 13 cm **12** 3 cm **13** 5 cm

14 b $14 - x$ **c** 8, 6 cm **15 b** $34 - x$ **c** 30, 4 cm

16 a $15 - x$ **b** 5, 10 cm **17 a** $11 - x$ **b** 4, 7 cm

18 a $13 - x$ **b** 5, 8 m **19** 4 m

20 3 cm **21 a** x^2 **b** $3x$ **c** 4 m

22 b $8x$ **c** $7x^2$ **d** 4 **e** 128 m^3 **23 a** $9x$ **b** x **c** 3, 6 m

24 a x^2 **b** $6x$ **c** 8 m **25 a** $x + 1, x + 4$ **b** 3 m **c** 4, 7 m

26 a $x + 5, x + 2$ **b** 4 m **c** 30 m

27 a $x + 6, x + 8$ **b** 2 m **c** 8, 10 m

28 a $8 + 2x, 10 + 2x$ **b** 2 cm **c** 88 cm^2

29 b $10 - 2x, 16 - 2x$ **c** 1 m **d** 48 m^2

30 a $x + 2$ **b** $(x + 2)^2$ **c** x^2 **d** 3 cm

Solution by factors

Part 7

All but the brightest pupils find difficult those quadratic equations having coefficients of x^2 greater than unity. Appreciation of how to expand brackets is required: for example, in this expansion,

$$(2x - 3)(x + 7) = 2x^2 + 14x - 3x - 21$$
$$= 2x^2 \quad + 11x \quad - 21.$$

The $2x^2$ and -21 terms can be called the "outer terms"

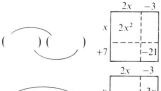

and the $+11x$ or "middle term" is a combination of two products.

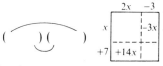

When factorising $2x^2 + 11x - 21$, the factors of 2 are 2×1 and the factors of -21 are $-21 \times +1$
$$+21 \times -1$$
$$+ 7 \times -3$$
$$\text{and} - 7 \times +3.$$

The investigation to decide how these factors combine to give $+11$ can be set out as follows:

where the products along the diagonals are combined using the number ladder until $-3 + 14 = +11$ is discovered. The two columns then give the entries in the brackets.

1 $-\frac{1}{2}, -1$ **2** $1, \frac{1}{3}$ **3** $-\frac{1}{5}, -1$ **4 a** $\frac{1}{2}, \frac{1}{2}$ **b** $1, \frac{1}{4}$

5 a $-\frac{1}{6}, -1$ **b** $-\frac{1}{3}, -\frac{1}{2}$ **6 a** $1, \frac{1}{8}$ **b** $\frac{1}{2}, \frac{1}{4}$ **7 a** $-\frac{1}{9}, -1$ **b** $-\frac{1}{3}, -\frac{1}{3}$

8 a $1\frac{2}{5}, 1$ **b** $7, \frac{1}{5}$ **9 a** $-\frac{6}{7}, -1$ **b** $-\frac{1}{7}, -6$ **c** $-\frac{3}{7}, -2$ **d** $-\frac{2}{7}, -3$

10 a $5, \frac{1}{3}$ **b** $10, \frac{1}{6}$ **c** $1\frac{2}{3}, 1$ **d** $3\frac{1}{3}, \frac{1}{2}$

11 a $-1, -1\frac{7}{8}$ **b** $-3, -\frac{5}{8}$ **c** $-\frac{3}{4}, -2\frac{1}{2}$

12 a $7, \frac{2}{9}$ **b** $2\frac{1}{3}, \frac{2}{3}$ **c** $1\frac{5}{9}, 1$ **13 a** $1, -\frac{1}{2}$ **b** $\frac{1}{2}, -1$

14 a $\frac{1}{5}, -1$ **b** $1, -\frac{1}{5}$ **15 a** $1, -\frac{1}{6}$ **b** $\frac{1}{3}, -\frac{1}{2}$ **c** $\frac{1}{2}, -\frac{1}{3}$

16 a $1\frac{1}{5}, -1$ **b** $1, -1\frac{1}{5}$ **c** $2, -\frac{3}{5}$ **17 a** $1, -1\frac{1}{7}$ **b** $-2, \frac{4}{7}$ **c** $-4, \frac{2}{7}$

18 a $12, -\frac{1}{3}$ **b** $3, -1\frac{1}{3}$ **c** $1\frac{1}{3}, -3$ **d** $\frac{2}{3}, -6$

19 a $1, -3\frac{3}{4}$ **b** $\frac{1}{4}, -15$ **c** $15, -\frac{1}{4}$ **20 a** $1, -7\frac{1}{2}$ **b** $5, -1\frac{1}{2}$ **c** $2\frac{1}{2}, -3$

21 a $1, -1\frac{1}{8}$ **b** $\frac{1}{8}, -9$ **c** $2\frac{1}{4}, -\frac{1}{2}$ **d** $1\frac{1}{2}, -\frac{3}{4}$

22 a $2, -\frac{5}{6}$ **b** $2\frac{1}{2}, -\frac{2}{3}$ **c** $3\frac{1}{3}, -\frac{1}{2}$ **23** $1\frac{1}{3}, -\frac{3}{4}$ **24** $2\frac{1}{2}, -\frac{4}{5}$

25 $1, \frac{1}{2}$ **26** $1, -\frac{1}{3}$ **27** $\frac{1}{2}, -\frac{1}{3}$ **28** $1\frac{1}{5}, -1$ **29** $4, \frac{2}{3}$

30 $\frac{2}{3}, -\frac{2}{5}$ **31** $1\frac{1}{2}, -1\frac{2}{5}$ **32** $1, \frac{1}{4}$ **33** $1\frac{1}{2}, -1\frac{2}{3}$ **34** $6, 4$

35 $1, \frac{3}{4}$ **36** $1\frac{2}{3}, -\frac{1}{2}$ **37** $-1, \frac{3}{4}$ **38** $4, \frac{1}{2}$ **39** $2, -1$

40 $6, -4$

Solution by formula

The derivation of the formula might be appreciated by the brighter pupil.

$$ax^2 + bx + c = 0$$

Divide by a

$$x^2 + \frac{b}{a}x + \frac{c}{a} = 0$$

Complete the square

$$\left(x + \frac{b}{2a}\right)^2 - \frac{b^2}{4a^2} + \frac{c}{a} = 0$$

Rearrange

$$\left(x + \frac{b}{2a}\right)^2 = \frac{b^2}{4a^2} - \frac{c}{a}$$

$$= \frac{b^2 - 4ac}{4a^2}$$

Square root

$$x + \frac{b}{2a} = \frac{\pm\sqrt{b^2 - 4ac}}{2a}$$

Subtract $\dfrac{b}{2a}$ from both sides

$$x = -\frac{b}{2a} \pm \frac{\sqrt{b^2 - 4ac}}{2a} = \frac{-b \pm \sqrt{b^2 - 4ac}}{2a}$$

Part 1

1 7, 4	**2** 5, 2	**3** $1\frac{1}{2}$, 1	**4** 3, $\frac{2}{3}$	**5** $-3, -5$
6 $-2, -7$	**7** $-1, -2\frac{1}{2}$	**8** $-\frac{1}{2}, -1\frac{1}{2}$	**9** 3, -8	**10** 2, -11
11 $1\frac{2}{5}, -2$	**12** $1\frac{1}{2}, -1\frac{2}{3}$	**13** 7, -3	**14** 11, -1	**15** 4, $-\frac{1}{2}$
16 $1\frac{1}{2}, -\frac{3}{4}$				

Part 2

1 7.65, 2.35	**2** 5.65, 0.35	**3** 1.68, 0.12	**4** No real solutions
5 $-6.70, -0.30$	**6** $-5.45, -0.55$	**7** $-1.5, -1.5$	**8** No real solutions
9 $-3.45, 1.45$	**10** $-1.62, 0.62$	**11** $-1.54, 0.87$	**12** $-0.88, 0.68$
13 $-1.45, 3.45$	**14** $-0.62, 1.62$	**15** $-0.86, 1.36$	**16** $-0.80, 2.80$

Part 3

1 4, -2.5	**2** 1, -1.67	**3** 1, 0.4
4 1.5, 0.5	**5** No real solutions	**6** $\frac{1}{3}, \frac{1}{3}$
7 $2\frac{1}{2}, 2\frac{1}{2}$	**8** $-2.57, 0.91$	**9** $-3.16, 0.16$
10 2.78, 0.72	**11** No real solutions	**12** No real solutions
13 $-4.12, 0.12$	**14** 2.29, -0.29	**15** $-6.16, 0.16$
16 0.44, 1.36	**17** $-4.24, 0.24$	**18** 3.78, 1.72
19 No real solutions	**20** 0.4, 0.4	

Solution by formula

Part 4

1 Two different	**2** Two different	**3** Two different	**4** Two different
5 One repeated	**6** One repeated	**7** None	**8** None
9 Two different	**10** Two different	**11** Two different	**12** One repeated
13 None	**14** One repeated	**15** None	**16** None
17 Two different	**18** Two different	**19** Two different	**20** Two different
21 Two different	**22** None	**23** One repeated	**24** Two different

Solution by graphical methods

Part 1

1 1, 4 **2** 2, 5 **3** 1, 6 **4** 0, 3 **5** 1

6 1, 5 **7** 3 **8** $\frac{1}{2}$, 4 **9** -2, 4 **10** -3, 2

Part 2

1 3, 1 **2** 4, 2 **3** 2, 2 **4** 6, 2

5 5, 1 **6** No solutions **7** 3, -1 **8** No solutions

9 -1, -1 **10** 3.8, -0.8 **11** 3.4, -1.4 **12** 1.6, -2.6

13 $1\frac{1}{2}$, $1\frac{1}{2}$ **14** $3\frac{1}{2}$, -1 **15** -2.35, 0.85 **16** -2, 4

17 0, 3 **18** 2.35, -0.85

Part 3

1 **a** 6, 2 **b** 7, 1 **c** 5, 3 **d** 7.74, 0.26
　　e -4

2 **a** 4, 2 **b** 5, 1 **c** 5.65, 0.35 **d** No points of intersection
　　e -1

3 **a** 1, -3 **b** 2, -4 **c** 0, -2 **d** 2.46, -4.46
　　e No points of intersection **f** -4

4 **a** 3, -2 **b** 4, -3 **c** 2, -1 **d** 3.54, -2.54
　　e No points of intersection **f** -6.25

5 **a** None exist **b** (i) 3, -1 (ii) 1, 1 (iii) 2.41, -0.41

6 **a** 1, 5 **b** (i) 2, 4 (ii) 5.65, 0.35 (iii) 3, 3

7 **a** 4, 0 **b** 1, 3 **c** 4.65, -0.65 **d** No solutions

8 **c** 1, 4 **9** **c** 2, 4 **10** **c** 5, 2 **11** **c** 2, -2

12 **b** 3, 1 **13** **b** 4, -1 **14** **b** 7, 2 **15** **b** $1\frac{1}{2}$

Solution by graphical methods

It is instructive to compare the methods using graph and formula.

The curve, (called a **parabola**), will intersect any straight line (and in particular the x-axis)

    either twice, in two distinct points,

    or   once, at a point where the line is a tangent to the curve,

    or   not at all.

These correspond to the quadratic equation having two, one or no real solutions, and the value of $b^2 - 4ac$ in the formula being positive, zero or negative respectively.

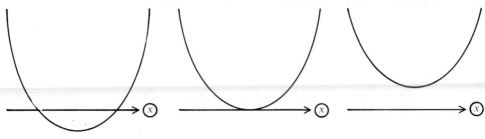

$b^2 - 4ac > 0$	$b^2 - 4ac = 0$	$b^2 - 4ac < 0$
two distinct roots	one double or repeated root	no real roots

Useful illustrations for classroom purposes are
$$x^2 - 4x + 3 = 0$$
$$x^2 - 4x + 4 = 0$$
$$x^2 - 4x + 5 = 0$$

two of the equations also lend themselves to factorisation.

Inequalities

Algebraic methods
Graphical methods

Algebraic methods

1 **a** $x \geqslant 3$ **b** $x \geqslant 0$ **c** $x > 1$ **d** $x > 4$
    e $x \geqslant -1$ **f** $x \leqslant 2$ **g** $x < 0$ **h** $x < -2$
    i $1 \leqslant x \leqslant 2$ **j** $1 < x < 2$ **k** $0 \leqslant x < 4$ **l** $-1 \leqslant x < 1$
    m $-2 < x < 0$ **n** $-3 \leqslant x \leqslant -1$

2 **a** number line (-4 to 4): solid dot at 2, arrow right
    b number line (-4 to 4): open dot at 2, arrow right
    c number line (-4 to 4): solid dot at 1, arrow right
    d number line (-4 to 4): solid dot at 1, arrow left
    e number line (-4 to 4): open dot at -1, arrow left
    f number line (-4 to 4): open dot at 1, arrow left
    g number line (-4 to 4): open dots at 2 and 3
    h number line (-4 to 4): open dots at 1 and 3
    i number line (-4 to 4): solid dots at 0 and 2
    j number line (-4 to 4): solid dots at 0 and 1
    k number line (-4 to 4): open dot at -1, solid dot at 2
    l number line (-4 to 4): solid dots at 0 and 3

3 **a** number line (-6 to 6): solid dot at -5 arrow left, solid dot at 5 arrow right
    b number line (-6 to 6): solid dots at -1 and 3
    c number line (-6 to 6): open dot at -3 arrow left, open dot at 2 arrow right
    d number line (-6 to 6): open dots at 0 and 1
    e number line (-6 to 6): arrow left, solid dot at 4
    f number line (-6 to 6): open dots at -1 and 5
    g number line (-6 to 6): open dots at -1 and 3
    h number line (-6 to 6): open dot at 4, arrow right
    i number line (-6 to 6): solid dots at 0 and 4
    j number line (-6 to 6): solid dots at -4 and 4
    k number line (-6 to 6): open dots at -3 and 0
    l number line (-6 to 6): arrow left, open dot at 0, arrow right

4 **a** $x \geqslant 4$ **b** $x \geqslant 9$ **c** $x < 5$ **d** $x < 4$ **e** $x > 8$ **f** $x \geqslant 4$
    g $x > 6$ **h** $x \leqslant 6$ **i** $x < 4\frac{1}{2}$ **j** $x > 7\frac{1}{2}$ **k** $x > 2\frac{1}{2}$ **l** $x \leqslant 3\frac{1}{2}$
    m $x < 2\frac{1}{2}$ **n** $x > 3$ **o** $x < 3$ **p** $x \geqslant 1\frac{1}{2}$ **q** $x < 4$ **r** $x > 5$
    s $x \leqslant 2$ **t** $x > 2$ **u** $x > 12$ **v** $x \leqslant 13$ **w** $x \geqslant 4$ **x** $x < 5$
    y $x > 5$ **z** $x \leqslant 9\frac{1}{2}$

5 **a** $x > 4$ **b** $x < 4$ **c** $x \geqslant 3$ **d** $x \leqslant 5$ **e** $x < 1$ **f** $x > 5$
    g $x > 4$ **h** $x \geqslant 3$ **i** $x \leqslant -2$ **j** $x < -3$ **k** $x \geqslant -5$ **l** $x > 0$
    m $x > -3$ **n** $x < -1$ **o** $x < 12$ **p** $x \geqslant 30$ **q** $x > 5$ **r** $x \leqslant -3$

6 **a** $x > -2$ **b** $x < -7$ **c** $x \leqslant -5$ **d** $x \geqslant -4$ **e** $x \leqslant -8$ **f** $x < -5$
    g $x > -2$ **h** $x > -4$ **i** $x \leqslant -2$ **j** $x \geqslant -6$ **k** $x \leqslant 2$ **l** $x < 3$
    m $x < 3$ **n** $x > 2$ **o** $x > -8$ **p** $x \leqslant -10$ **q** $x < -15$
    r $x \geqslant -12$ **s** $x < -6$ **t** $x \leqslant -40$ **u** $x \geqslant -6$ **v** $x > 24$
    w $x \leqslant -3$ **x** $x \geqslant -2$ **y** $x < -4$ **z** $x \leqslant -2\frac{1}{2}$

7 **a** $x < -1$ **b** $x > -4$ **c** $x > -2$ **d** $x > -3$ **e** $x > 11$
    f $x \leqslant -3$ **g** $x \geqslant -2$ **h** $x < -1\frac{1}{2}$ **i** $x < 1$ **j** $x \geqslant -1\frac{1}{2}$
    k $x > 0$ **l** $x > -\frac{1}{2}$ **m** $x > -10$ **n** $x \leqslant -7$ **o** $x > -4$
    p $x > -9$ **q** $x > 12$ **r** $x > 50$ **s** $x > -2$

Algebraic methods

8
  a $-3 \leqslant x \leqslant 3$
    b $-4 \leqslant x \leqslant 4$
    c $-9 \leqslant x \leqslant 9$

  d $-2 \leqslant x \leqslant 2$
    e $-10 < x < 10$
    f $-12 < x < 12$

  g $-8 < x < 8$
    h $-1 < x < 1$
    i $-5 \leqslant x \leqslant 5$

  j $-2 \leqslant x \leqslant 2$
    k $-6 \leqslant x \leqslant 6$
    l $-4 \leqslant x \leqslant 4$

  m $x \geqslant 3$ or $x \leqslant -3$
  n $x \geqslant 7$ or $x \leqslant -7$
  o $x \geqslant 8$ or $x \leqslant -8$

  p $x \geqslant 12$ or $x \leqslant -12$
  q $x \geqslant 5$ or $x \leqslant -5$
  r $x > 5$ or $x < -5$

  s $x > 1$ or $x < -1$
  t $x > 10$ or $x < -10$
  u $-1 \leqslant x \leqslant 1$

  v $-3 \leqslant x \leqslant 3$
    w $-1 < x < 1$
    x $-2 \leqslant x \leqslant 2$

  y $x > 7$ or $x < -7$
  z $x \geqslant 4$ or $x \leqslant -4$

9

10 4   **11** 4   **12** 3   **13** 5

14 -2 **15** 1, 2, 3, 4   **16** 4, 5, 6, 7   **17** 3, 4, 5, 6

18 18, 19, 20, 21

Graphical methods

1 $1 \leqslant x \leqslant 3$
    2 $2 \leqslant x \leqslant 4$
    3 $x \leqslant -1$ or $x \geqslant 2$

4 $x > 1$ or $x < -1\frac{1}{2}$
    5 $-1 \leqslant x \leqslant 3$
    6 $-2 \leqslant x \leqslant 1$

7 $x < -2$ or $x > 2$
    8 $-1 \leqslant x \leqslant 1$ or $x \geqslant 3$
    9 $x \leqslant -2$ or $0 \leqslant x \leqslant 2$

10 $x < -3$ or $0 < x < 1$
  11 $x > 2$
    12 $-2 < x < 1$ or $x > 1$

13 $1 \leqslant x \leqslant 4$
    14 $1 \leqslant x \leqslant 2$
    15 $x \geqslant 3$ or $x \leqslant -1$

16 $x \geqslant 1$ or $x \leqslant -2$
  17 $1 < x < 3$
    18 $x \geqslant 2$ or $x \leqslant 1$

19
  a $2 < x < 3$
    20
  a $1 < x < 4$
    21
  c   (i) $2 < x < 3$

  b $x > 3$ or $x < 2$
      b $x > 4$ or $x < 1$
          (ii) $x > 3$ or $x < 2$

  c $x = 2$ or $x = 3$
      c $x = 1$ or $x = 4$
          (iii) $x = 2$ or $x = 3$

22
  c   (i) $2 < x < 5$
    23
  c   (i) $1 < x < 4$
    24
  c   (i) $\frac{1}{2} < x < 4$

     (ii) $x > 5$ or $x < 2$
       (ii) $x > 4$ or $x < 1$
       (ii) $x > 4$ or $x < \frac{1}{2}$

     (iii) $x = 5$ or $x = 2$
      (iii) $x = 4$ or $x = 1$
      (iii) $x = 4$ or $x = \frac{1}{2}$

25
  c   (i) $2\frac{1}{2} < x < 4$

     (ii) $x > 4$ or $x < 2\frac{1}{2}$

     (iii) $x = 4$ or $x = 2\frac{1}{2}$

Formulae

Simple substitution
Harder substitution
Area and volume formulae
Squares and square roots
Numerical rearrangement of scientific formulae
Flow diagrams and rearrangement of formulae

Simple substitution

1 **a** 9 **b** 10 **c** 13 **d** 17 **e** 7 **f** 6 **g** 4
   h 75 **i** 14 **j** 10 **k** 20 **l** 50 **m** 20 **n** 20
   o 18 **p** 3 **q** 2 **r** 7 **s** $3\frac{1}{2}$ **t** 3

2 **a** 8 **b** 0 **c** −2 **d** −5 **e** 0 **f** 10 **g** −9
   h 32 **i** 40 **j** 52 **k** 100 **l** 32 **m** 64 **n** 3
   o 9 **p** 8 **q** 4 **r** 12 **s** 4 **t** 8

3 **a** 3 **b** 13 **c** 48 **d** −5 **e** −6 **f** 13 **g** −5
   h 0 **i** 1 **j** 30 **k** 72 **l** 55 **m** 10 **n** 8
   o −6 **p** 4 **q** 3 **r** 4 **s** 7 **t** 5

4 **a** 18 **b** 40 **c** 5 **d** 5 **e** 4.8 **f** 67.5
   g 24 **h** 4 **i** 4 **j** $3\frac{1}{3}$ **k** 139.1 **l** 18
   m 28 **n** 100 **o** 8 **p** 24 **q** 12.5 **r** 745
   s 6 **t** 2

5 **a** 30 **b** 5 **c** 4 **d** 11.76 **e** 45 **f** 80
   g $1\frac{1}{4}$ **h** 19.6 **i** 78.4

6 **a** 6 **b** 2 **c** $3\frac{1}{2}$ **d** $5\frac{1}{3}$ **e** $1\frac{1}{4}$ **f** $2\frac{1}{2}$
   g 1 **h** 4 **i** 6 **j** 3 **k** $2\frac{1}{2}$

7 **a** 14 **b** 43 **c** 10 **d** 12 **e** 2 **f** 4
   g 10 **h** 20 **i** $10\frac{1}{2}$ **j** $17\frac{1}{2}$ **k** 14 **l** 0
   m $\frac{1}{2}$ **n** 2.52 **o** 8.14 **p** 24 **q** 16 **r** 65
   s 6 **t** 6 **u** 200 **v** 6

8 **a** 14 **b** 12 **c** 11 **d** $9\frac{1}{2}$

9 **a** 15 **b** 30 **c** 50 **d** 60

10 **a** 2 **b** 1.2 **c** 24 **d** 18

11 **a** 24 **b** 24 **c** 4 **d** 4

12 **a** 18 **b** 12 **c** 60 **d** 3

13 **a** 18 **b** 12.56   **14** **a** 96 **b** 45 **c** 14

15 **a** 144 **b** $4\frac{1}{2}$ **c** 753.6   **16** **a** 360 **b** 90 **c** 97.5

17 **a** 6 **b** 6 **c** 4.8   **18** **a** 7 **b** 9 **c** 5

19 **a** 2 **b** $\frac{1}{2}$ **20** **a** 60 **b** 188.4

21 **a** 1.10 **b** 0.894   **22** **a** £75·26 **b** £66·$12\frac{1}{2}$

Harder substitution

Part 1

1 a $3\frac{1}{2}$ b $1\frac{1}{2}$ c 2   d $-2\frac{1}{2}$ e $-3\frac{1}{2}$
   f 32   g 64   h 8   i 4   j -12

2 a 2   b -5 c 1   d 10   e 6
   f 6   g -4 h 38   i 19   j 1

3 a $6\frac{1}{2}$ b $-4\frac{1}{2}$ c $\frac{1}{2}$ d $11\frac{1}{2}$ e -4
   f -3 g $25\frac{1}{4}$ h $38\frac{1}{2}$ i $3\frac{1}{2}$ j 15

4 a 3   b -9 c 6   d 20   e -3
   f 13   g 0   h 0   i 18   j 36

5 a 16   b -25 c -10 d 14   e -4
   f -17 g -25 h 4

6 a 50   b 14   c 59   d 5   e -4
   f -22 g 42.8   h 28.4

7 a 0   b 10   c -10 d -15 e -20
   f -50 g $2\frac{2}{9}$ h $-1\frac{1}{9}$

8 a 5   b 12   c 6   d 1   e 12
   f 7   g 7   h 4

9 a 48   b 95   c 48   d 56   e -12
   f 36   g 55   h -140

10 a 2   b $1\frac{1}{2}$ c -40 d -6 e -10
    f 24   g -5 h -3

11 a 69   b 44   c 4   d -10 e -2
    f 180   g -33 h -120

12 a 2   b 3   c 4   d $1\frac{1}{3}$ e $1\frac{1}{2}$

13 a 19   b 3   c -2 d -6 e -2
    f 3

14 a 10   b 1   c -6 d 6   e -15

15 a 12   b -3 c -15 d 12   e -3

16 a 66   b 21   c -15 d 66   e 21

17 a 18   b -3 c 2   d -6

18 a 2   b -3 c -7 d 9

19 a 8   b -2 c 16   d 26

20 a 28   b 6   c 3   d 0

Harder substitution

21	**a**	1	**b**	-8	**c**	25	**d**	56	
22	**a**	15	**b**	-1	**c**	-3	**d**	$-2\frac{1}{2}$	
23	**a**	18	**b**	-21	**c**	8	**d**	-25	**e** 3
	f	$\frac{1}{2}$	**g**	-3	**h**	3			
24	**a**	8	**b**	6	**c**	42	**d**	5	**e** 3
	f	3	**g**	-4	**h**	8			
25	**a**	-6	**b**	12	**c**	34	**d**	100	**e** 160
	f	-2	**g**	± 4	**h**	± 9			
26	**a**	18	**b**	-1	**c**	Impossible	**d**	6	**e** ± 7
	f	± 3	**g**	2	**h**	6			

Part 2 With decimals and use of square and square-root tables

1	**a**	15·3	**b**	4.59	**c**	15·1	**2**	**a**	1.04	**b**	0.9		
3	**a**	1.375	**b**	54.1	**4**	**a**	1.24	**b**	12.75	**5**	**a**	2.85	**b** 1.2
6	**a**	326·56	**b**	1168.08	**7**	**a**	10.56	**b**	34.86	**c**	10.66		
8	**a**	1.92		**b**	-23.68		**c**	-18.9		**d**	-0.18		
9	**a**	23.1	**b**	97.6	**c**	26·3	**10**	**a**	32.7	**b**	251.4		
11	**a**	6.75	**b**	21.3	**12**	**a**	2.5	**b**	1.73	**13**	**a**	7.84	**b** 8.88
14	**a**	60.3	**b**	10.6	**15**	**a**	22	**b**	6·58	**16**	**a**	1.72	**b** 4.67
17	**a**	1.07	**b**	1.4	**18**	**a**	263	**b**	154				

Area and volume formulae

Part 1

1	$a = 4\,\text{cm}$	**2**	$b = 5\,\text{cm}$	**3**	$c = 8\,\text{cm}$	**4**	$d = 6\,\text{cm}$	**5**	$e = 12\,\text{cm}$
6	**a** 7 cm	**b** $3\frac{1}{2}$ cm	**c** $12\frac{1}{2}$ cm	**7**	**a** $7\frac{1}{2}$ cm	**b** $2\frac{2}{3}$ cm			
8	$f = 4\,\text{cm}$	**9**	$g = 7\,\text{cm}$	**10**	$h = 5\frac{1}{2}\,\text{cm}$	**11**	$i = 5\frac{1}{2}\,\text{cm}$	**12**	$= 3\frac{1}{3}\,\text{cm}$
13	**a** $7\frac{1}{2}$ cm	**b** $5\frac{1}{3}$ cm	**c** $5\frac{1}{4}$ cm	**14**	**a** $9\frac{3}{4}$ cm	**b** $3\frac{1}{3}$ cm			
15	$k = 5\,\text{cm}$	**16**	$l = 5\,\text{cm}$	**17**	$m = 4\,\text{cm}$	**18**	$n = 6\,\text{cm}$	**19**	$p = 8\,\text{cm}$
20	**a** $7\frac{1}{2}$ cm	**b** 7 cm	**c** 4 cm	**21**	**a** 8 cm	**b** 6 cm			
22	$q = 4\,\text{cm}$	**23**	$r = 3\,\text{cm}$	**24**	$s = 5\,\text{cm}$	**25**	$t = 7\,\text{cm}$	**26**	$u = 6\,\text{cm}$
27	**a** $6\frac{1}{2}$ cm	**b** 9 cm	**c** 8 cm	**d** 6 cm	**e** 6 cm			
28	**a** 5 cm	**b** 10 cm	**c** 2 cm	**d** 4 cm	**e** 6 cm			
	f 7 cm	**g** 12 cm	**h** 9 cm	**i** 11 cm	**j** 13 cm			
29	**a** 4.8 cm	**b** 7.35 cm	**c** 6·4 cm	**d** 4.9 cm	**e** 9.7 cm			
	f 2.45 cm	**g** 2.65 cm	**h** 2.55 cm	**i** 2.35 cm	**j** 7.25 cm			
	k 8.75 cm	**l** 5·15 cm						
30	**a** 6 cm	**b** 6 cm	**c** 9 cm	**d** $4\frac{1}{2}$ cm	**e** $2\frac{1}{2}$ cm	**f** $5\frac{1}{3}$ cm
31	**a** 3 cm	**b** 5 cm	**c** 4 cm	**d** $5\frac{1}{2}$ cm	**e** $3\frac{1}{2}$ cm	**f** $2\frac{1}{3}$ cm
32	**a** 8 cm	**b** 8 cm	**c** 6 cm	**d** 3 cm	**e** $3\frac{1}{2}$ cm	**f** $2\frac{1}{2}$ cm

Area and volume formulae

33 **a** 6 cm   **b** 20 cm   **c** 3 cm   **d** 4 cm   **e** 7 cm   **f** 9 cm

34 **a** 10 cm   **b** 6 cm   **c** 8 cm   **d** 7 cm   **e** $2\frac{1}{2}$ cm   **f** $6\frac{1}{2}$ cm

35 **a** 2 cm   **b** 2 cm   **c** 1 cm   **d** 6 cm   **e** 4 cm   **f** 3 cm
     g 3 cm   **h** 4 cm

Part 2 Using decimals

1 $a - 3.67$ cm   **2** $b - 2.1$ cm   **3** $c = 3.2$ cm   **4** $d = 1.74$ cm   **5** $e = 2.15$ cm

6 **a** 1.35 cm   **b** 0.35 cm   **c** 1.26 cm   **7** **a** 3.26 cm   **b** 2.4 cm

8 $f = 1.4$ cm   **9** $g = 2.24$ cm **10** $h = 1.25$ cm **11** $i = 1.24$ cm **12** $j = 1.35$ cm

13 **a** 3.7 cm   **b** 3.4 cm   **c** 0.35 cm   **14** **a** 1.26 cm   **b** 2.05 cm

15 $k = 2.4$ cm **16** $l = 0.6$ cm   **17** $m = 1.5$ cm **18** $n = 0.8$ cm **19** $p = 1.8$ cm

20 **a** 2.4 cm   **b** 3.6 cm   **c** 2.24 cm   **21** **a** 3.24 cm   **b** 1.05 cm

22 $q = 1.45$ cm **23** $r = 1.24$ cm **24** $s = 0.52$ cm **25** $t = 0.64$ cm **26** $u = 0.62$ cm

27 **a** 1.2 cm   **b** 1.25 cm   **c** 1.34 cm   **d** 4.2 cm   **e** 1.65 cm

28 **a** 3 cm   **b** 2 cm   **c** 5 cm   **d** 6 cm   **e** 8 cm   **f** 12 cm
     g 4 cm   **h** 7 cm   **i** 11 cm   **j** 9 cm   **k** 13 cm

29 **a** 5 cm   **b** 4 cm   **c** 2 cm   **d** 6 cm   **e** 11 cm   **f** 12 cm
     g 8 cm   **h** 3 cm   **i** 7 cm   **j** 9 cm   **k** 13 cm

30 **a** 3.4 cm   **b** 3.5 cm   **c** 4.7 cm   **d** 4.8 cm   **e** 5.8 cm   **f** 6.6 cm
     g 7.2 cm   **h** 4 cm   **i** 5 cm   **j** 8.1 cm   **k** 9.3 cm   **l** 4.2 cm

31 90 cm   **32** 60 cm   **33** 1.24 cm   **34** 1.35 cm

35 **a** 0.8 cm   **b** 0.16 cm   **c** 0.8 cm   **d** 1.4 cm   **e** 1.7 cm   **f** 0.8 cm
     g 1 cm   **h** 0.9 cm

Part 3 Using fractions

Two layouts of the working are possible when using fractions, indicating two methods of explanation.

For example, for the first rectangle in this exercise, substitution into the formula $A = l\,w$ gives

$$\frac{3}{4} = \frac{9}{10}a.$$

Then it can be said

either "the length a will be found by dividing the area by the width"

$$\text{giving } a = \frac{\frac{3}{4}}{\frac{9}{10}};$$

or, thinking more algebraically, "multiply both sides by 10 and divide both sides by 9"

$$\text{giving } \frac{\cancel{10}^{\,①}}{\cancel{9}_{\,①}} \times \frac{\cancel{9}^{\,①}}{\cancel{10}_{\,①}} \times a = \frac{10}{9} \times \frac{3}{4}$$

The second of these methods is probably the more useful line of approach for general purposes.

Area and volume formulae

1 $a = \frac{2}{6}$ cm   2 $b = 1\frac{1}{8}$ cm   3 $c = 2\frac{2}{5}$ cm   4 $d = \frac{3}{8}$ cm   5 $e = \frac{3}{5}$ cm

6 a $2\frac{2}{3}$ cm   b $4\frac{1}{2}$ cm   7 a $1\frac{7}{8}$ cm   b $1\frac{7}{9}$ cm   c $3\frac{1}{3}$ cm

8 $f = \frac{9}{10}$ cm   9 $g = 1\frac{7}{8}$ cm   10 $h = 1\frac{1}{8}$ cm   11 $i = 1\frac{3}{5}$ cm   12 $j = 1.2$ cm

13 a $2\frac{2}{3}$ cm   b $3\frac{3}{4}$ cm   14 a $3\frac{3}{8}$ cm   b $3\frac{1}{8}$ cm   c $2\frac{2}{5}$ cm

15 $k = 1\frac{1}{5}$ cm   16 $l = \frac{8}{9}$ cm   17 $m = \frac{9}{10}$ cm   18 $n = 1\frac{3}{5}$ cm   19 $p = 1\frac{1}{11}$ cm

20 a $3\frac{1}{5}$ cm   b $4\frac{1}{2}$ cm   21 a $5\frac{1}{3}$ cm   b $9\frac{3}{5}$ cm   c $2\frac{1}{12}$ cm

22 $q = 2\frac{2}{3}$ cm   23 $r = 3\frac{1}{3}$ cm   24 $s = 5\frac{1}{3}$ cm   25 $t = 1\frac{2}{7}$ cm   26 $u = 6\frac{2}{3}$ cm

27 a $6\frac{2}{3}$ cm   b $1\frac{11}{15}$ cm   c $1\frac{3}{5}$ cm   d $3\frac{3}{7}$ cm   e $3\frac{1}{5}$ cm

28 a $3\frac{1}{2}$ cm   b $1\frac{1}{2}$ cm   c $3\frac{1}{4}$ cm   d $2\frac{1}{2}$ cm   e $4\frac{3}{4}$ cm
   f $4\frac{1}{2}$ cm   g $2\frac{1}{8}$ cm   h $3\frac{2}{3}$ cm

29 a 2 cm   b $\frac{1}{2}$ cm   c $3\frac{1}{2}$ cm   d $1\frac{3}{4}$ cm   e 7 cm
   f 3 cm   g $1\frac{1}{2}$ cm   h 4 cm

30 a $1\frac{1}{6}$ cm   b 1 cm   c 4 cm   d 7 cm   e 14 cm
   f 21 cm

Part 4 The circumference of a circle

1 a 7 cm   b 14 cm   c 21 cm   d 28 cm   e 2 cm   f 3 cm
   g $2\frac{4}{5}$ cm   h $1\frac{5}{9}$ cm   i $1\frac{2}{5}$ cm   j $2\frac{1}{3}$ cm   k $1\frac{1}{5}$ cm   l $4\frac{1}{5}$ cm
   m $3\frac{1}{9}$ cm   n $1\frac{3}{4}$ cm   o $1\frac{1}{6}$ cm   p $5\frac{1}{4}$ cm

2 a $1\frac{2}{5}$ cm   b $\frac{7}{9}$ cm   c $1\frac{1}{6}$ cm   d $\frac{7}{10}$ cm   e $1\frac{1}{20}$ cm   f $1\frac{5}{16}$ cm
   g $\frac{3}{4}$ cm   h $\frac{7}{8}$ cm   i $\frac{7}{12}$ cm   j $\frac{1}{4}$ cm   k $4\frac{3}{8}$ cm   l $2\frac{11}{12}$ cm
   m $1\frac{1}{4}$ cm   n $2\frac{1}{4}$ cm   o $2\frac{1}{10}$ cm   p $2\frac{4}{5}$ cm

3 a 1.2 m   b 2.1 m   c 1.5 m   d 1.25 m   e 2.25 m   f 3.5 m
   g 1.43 m   h 3.1 m   i 2.35 m   j 4.2 m   k 4.04 m   l 2.32 m
   m 5.25 m   n 5.54 m   o 0.621 m   p 0.104 m

4 a 1.1 m   b 1.2 m   c 1.25 m   d 2.25 m   e 2.13 m   f 13.4 m
   g 21.7 m   h 11.6 m   i 33.4 m   j 0.553 m

5 a 2.58 m   b 3.03 m   c 1.87 m   d 6.33 m   e 6.24 m   f 17.5 m
   g 28.6 m   h 65.3 m   i 92.3 m   j 58.9 m   k 532 m   l 2700 m
   m 1190 m   n 0.208 m   o 0.3 m   p 0.176 m

6 a 1.27 m   b 1.36 m   c 1.44 m   d 4.25 m   e 8.04 m   f 12.9 m
   g 51.7 m   h 113 m   i 342 m   j 1080 m   k 1.54 m   l 0.123 m

Area and volume formulae

Problems

7 8.44 m   **8 a** 25 m   **b** 12.5 m   **9** 5.86 km **10 a** 30 cm   **b** 15 cm
11 $24\frac{1}{2}$ cm   **12** $5\frac{1}{4}$ cm   **13** $22\frac{3}{4}$ cm   **14** 1.75 cm   **15** 65 cm
16 a 10.2 cm   **b** 3.25 cm   **17 a** 14 cm   **b** 4.46 cm   **c** 2.23 cm
18 a 6.28 cm   **b** 2 cm   **19** 13 000 km, 6500 km
20 a 21.5 m   **b** 6.85 m   **c** 3.42 m

Part 5 The area of a circle

1 a $\frac{1}{3}$ cm   **b** $\frac{1}{2}$ cm   **c** $\frac{2}{3}$ cm   **d** 2 cm   **e** 3 cm
   f $3\frac{1}{2}$ cm   **g** $1\frac{1}{2}$ cm   **h** $2\frac{1}{3}$ cm   **i** $1\frac{3}{4}$ cm   **j** $1\frac{2}{5}$ cm
   k $1\frac{3}{11}$ cm   **l** $2\frac{1}{2}$ cm

2 a 2 cm   **b** 3 cm   **c** 5 cm   **d** 4 cm   **e** 10 cm
   f 6 cm   **g** 12 cm   **h** 9 cm

3 a 5.2 cm   **b** 5.9 cm   **c** 4.74 cm   **d** 5.52 cm   **e** 2.74 cm
   f 4.62 cm   **g** 9.01 cm   **h** 7.23 cm   **i** 11.5 cm   **j** 12.5 cm
   k 17.4 cm   **l** 22.5 cm   **m** 25.6 cm   **n** 35.4 cm   **o** 50.2 cm
   p 60.5 cm

4 a 1.59 cm   **b** 1.74 cm   **c** 1.52 cm   **d** 1.19 cm   **e** 2.52 cm
   f 3.06 cm   **g** 2.14 cm   **h** 3.56 cm   **i** 3.93 cm   **j** 4.32 cm
   k 5.31 cm   **l** 9.13 cm   **m** 8.92 cm   **n** 9.89 cm   **o** 14.2 cm
   p 12.6 cm   **q** 16.5 cm   **r** 22.1 cm   **s** 37.7 cm   **t** 52.6 cm

Problems

5 1.2 m   **6** 2.55 m   **7** 7.88 cm, 15.8 cm **8** 1.4 cm, 2.8 cm
9 7 cm   **10** 3 cm   **11** $2\frac{1}{3}$ cm   **12** $1\frac{3}{4}$ cm
13 a 17 cm   **b** 34 cm   **14 a** 15.2 cm   **b** 30.4 m   **15** $10\frac{1}{2}$ cm^2
16 area = 750 cm^2, radius = 15.5 cm, diameter = 31 cm
17 a 85.2 cm^2 **b** 5.21 cm   **18 a** 33 cm^2 **b** 3.24 cm
19 a 6   **b** 129 cm^2 **c** 6.41 cm   **20 a** 284 cm^2 **b** 9.51 cm

Part 6 Arcs and sectors

1 a 60°   **b** 45°   **c** 20°   **d** 90°
   e 120°   **f** 270°   **g** 30°   **h** 140°

2 a $4\frac{2}{3}$ cm   **b** $4\frac{3}{8}$ cm   **c** $3\frac{3}{5}$ cm   **d** $11\frac{1}{4}$ cm
   e $1\frac{1}{2}$ cm   **f** $6\frac{1}{8}$ cm   **g** $6\frac{3}{4}$ cm   **h** $1\frac{7}{8}$

3 a 90°   **b** 120°   **c** 45°   **d** 180°
   e 72°   **f** 270°   **g** 240°   **h** 144°

Area and volume formulae

4 a 2 cm   **b** 5 cm   **c** 3 cm   **d** 12 cm

   e 15 cm   **f** 6 cm   **g** 4 cm   **h** 10 cm

5 $\angle XOY' = 120°$ **6** 69°   **7** 15.8 cm   **8 a** $OP = OQ = 3\frac{1}{2}$ cm   **b** 90°

9 a 280°   **b** 315°   **c** 105°   **d** 126°

   e 105°   **f** 45°   **g** $157\frac{1}{2}°$ **h** 240°

10 a 9 cm   **b** 7 cm   **c** 3 cm   **d** 4 cm

   e $1\frac{1}{2}$ cm   **f** $3\frac{1}{2}$ cm   **g** $4\frac{2}{3}$ cm   **h** $2\frac{1}{2}$ cm

11 a 30°   **b** 45°   **c** 180°   **d** 90°

   e 120°   **f** 144°   **g** 140°   **h** 240°

12 a 2.42 cm   **b** 2.86 cm   **c** 4.65 cm   **d** 4.08 cm

   e 5.69 cm   **f** 4.03 cm   **g** 5.17 cm   **h** 3.85 cm

13 210°   **14** 120°   **15** 9 m   **16** 10.4 km

Part 7

This exercise gives practice in choosing the correct formula and substituting into it. Practice at rearranging the volume formulae is left until parts 8 and 9.

1 36 cm³   **2** 12 cm³   **3** 240 cm³   **4** 80 cm³

5 462 cm³   **6** 154 cm³   **7** 90 cm³   **8** 96 cm³

9 20 cm³   **10** 1099 cm³   **11** 96 cm³   **12** 1407 cm³

13 1436 cm³   **14** 904 cm³   **15** $42\frac{2}{3}$ cm³   **16** 62.9 cm³

Using fractions

17 30 cm³   **18** 10 cm³   **19** 16 cm³   **20** $5\frac{1}{3}$ cm³

21 a $43\frac{1}{5}$ cm³   **b** 495 cm³   **c** 165 cm³   **d** 11 cm³   **e** $46\frac{1}{5}$ cm³   **f** 5 cm³

22 308.7 cm³   **23** 523 cm³   **24** 15 160 cm³   **25** 136 cm³

26 877 cm³   **27** 344 cm³   **28** 217 cm³   **29** 310 cm³   **30** 53 600 cm³

31 a 5 litres   **b** $6\frac{1}{2}$ litres   **c** 3 litres

Compound bodies

32 108π **33** 69π **34** 192π **35** 20π

36 99π **37** 63π **38** 408π **39** $11\frac{1}{3}\pi$

40 90π **41** 144π **42** 265π **43** 126π

44 $40\frac{2}{3}\pi$ **45** $37\frac{2}{3}\pi$ **46** 286 m³   **47** 282 cm³

48 1434 cm³ (Assumed that cone and cylinder are complete; however, they overlap at the joint, so the volume would be less)

Area and volume formulae

49 **a** 6 cm   **b** 75.4 cm^3 **c** 603 cm^3 **d** 528 cm^3

50 **a** 52 987.5 cm^3 **b** 15 700 cm^3 **c** 37 287.5 cm^3

51 **a** 122 m^2 **b** 1890 m^3 **c** 15.1 m

52 **a** 40.5 cm^2 **b** 607.5 cm^3 **53** 1595 cm^3

Part 8

1 **a** 4 cm   **b** 7 cm   **c** 5 cm   **d** 6 cm   **e** $2\frac{1}{2}$ cm   **f** $5\frac{1}{2}$ cm
   g $8\frac{1}{2}$ cm   **h** $5\frac{1}{2}$ cm

2 **a** 3 cm   **b** 2 cm   **c** 5 cm   **d** 5 cm   **e** $4\frac{1}{2}$ cm   **f** $3\frac{1}{2}$ cm

3 **a** $1\frac{1}{2}$ cm   **b** $3\frac{3}{4}$ cm   **c** $1\frac{11}{16}$ cm   **d** $3\frac{3}{4}$ cm

4 **a** $1\frac{1}{3}$ cm   **b** $16\frac{1}{5}$ cm   **c** $5\frac{1}{3}$ cm   **d** $2\frac{1}{10}$ cm

5 **a** $1\frac{3}{7}$ cm   **b** $1\frac{3}{11}$ cm   **c** $1\frac{5}{11}$ cm   **d** $12\frac{1}{2}$ cm   **e** $4\frac{2}{3}$ cm   **f** $2\frac{1}{4}$ cm
   g $9\frac{1}{3}$ cm   **h** $1\frac{2}{5}$ cm

6 **a** 2 cm   **b** 5 cm   **c** 3 cm   **d** $6\frac{1}{4}$ cm   **e** $1\frac{1}{2}$ cm   **f** $1\frac{1}{2}$ cm
   g $2\frac{1}{2}$ cm   **h** $\frac{1}{2}$ cm

7 **a** 5 cm   **b** 3 cm   **c** 5 cm   **d** 2.5 cm   **e** 4 cm   **f** 5 cm

8 **a** 6 cm   **b** 4 cm   **c** 5 cm   **d** 2 cm   **e** 5 cm   **f** 8 cm

9 **a** $2\frac{1}{7}$ cm   **b** $3\frac{1}{3}$ cm   **c** $\frac{2}{3}$ cm   **d** $\frac{3}{4}$ cm   **e** $1\frac{7}{9}$ cm   **f** $2\frac{5}{8}$ cm

10 **a** 4 cm   **b** 6 cm   **c** 6 cm   **d** 8 cm   **e** 5.1 cm   **f** $2\frac{1}{2}$ cm

11 **a** $7\frac{1}{2}$ cm   **b** $5\frac{1}{3}$ cm   **c** $4\frac{4}{5}$ cm   **d** $3\frac{1}{3}$ cm   **e** $12\frac{1}{2}$ cm   **f** $4\frac{4}{5}$ cm

12 **a** 6 cm   **b** 9 cm   **c** 12 cm   **d** $1\frac{1}{2}$ cm   **e** $3\frac{1}{2}$ cm   **f** $1\frac{2}{3}$ cm

13 **a** $1\frac{3}{5}$ cm   **b** $3\frac{3}{5}$ cm   **c** $\frac{4}{5}$ cm   **d** $5\frac{1}{3}$ cm   **e** 3 cm   **f** 4 cm
   g $1\frac{1}{2}$ cm   **h** $2\frac{1}{2}$ cm

14 **a** $4\frac{2}{3}$ cm   **b** $5\frac{1}{4}$ cm   **c** 30 cm   **d** 1 cm   **e** 9 cm   **f** 49 cm
   g 9 cm   **h** $1\frac{1}{2}$ cm

15 **a** 3 cm   **b** 2 cm   **c** $1\frac{1}{2}$ cm   **d** $3\frac{1}{2}$ cm

Part 9 Rearrangement using logarithms or a calculator

1 **a** 2.097 cm   **b** 1.984 cm   **c** 4.375 cm

2 **a** 4.091 cm^2 **b** 6.199 cm^2 **c** 6.684 cm^2

3 **a** 3.824 cm   **b** 3.744 cm   **c** 5.133 cm

4 **a** 8.897 cm^2 **b** 6.806 cm^2 **c** 7.604 cm^2

5 **a** 2.03 cm   **b** 1.47 cm   **c** 3.193 cm

6 4.584 cm   **7** **a** 2.279 cm   **b** 4.444 cm

8 **a** 7.382 cm   **b** 4.724 cm   **c** 12.545 cm

9 12.109 cm   **10** 13.581 cm   **11** 38.113 cm

12 **a** 2.055 cm   **b** 4.798 cm   **c** 0.159 cm

Area and volume formulae

13 a 15.588 cm   **b** 5.293 cm

14 a 5.996 cm   **b** 8.453 cm   **c** 3.881 cm

15 10.525 cm   **16 a** 1.444 cm   **b** 4.863 cm   **c** 3.077 cm

17 a 8.518 cm   **b** 12.495 cm

18 a 3.993 cm   **b** 7.162 cm   **c** 13.497 cm

19 13.555 cm   **20 a** 2 cm   **b** 3.717 cm

21 a 7.071 cm   **b** 6.205 cm   **c** 10.244 cm

22 a 3.462 cm   **b** 12.806 cm

23 a 8.55 cm   **b** 18.171 cm   **c** 13.925 cm

24 15.467 cm

Part 10

1 3.21 m   **2** 2.39 m   **3** 15.2 m   **4** 86.1 cm   **5** 2.23 m

6 14.2 cm   **7** 4.5 cm   **8** 55 cm   **9** 1.27 cm   **10** 1.2 cm

11 3.21 cm   **12** 11.7 cm   **13** 11.3 cm   **14** 5.65 cm   **15** 15.1 cm

16 a 410 cm^3 **b** 7.23 cm   **17** 6.41 cm   **18** 3.88 m   **19** 1.3 mm

20 2.16 cm   **21** 22.7 cm   **22** 55.8 cm   **23** 11.3 cm   **24** 4.52 cm

25 4.75 m   **26** 56.5 cm   **27** 2.59 cm   **28** 3.77 m   **29** 16.1 cm

30 1.2 cm, 2.4 cm   **31** 78.2 cm   **32 a** 6 litres   **b** 11.3 cm

33 6.79 m   **34 a** 367.5 cm^3 **b** 1.2 cm

35 a 16 800 cm^3 (16.8 litres)   **b** 1.29 cm   **36 a** 42.8 cm^3 **b** 6.96 cm

37 a 229 cm^3 **b** 6.12 cm   **38 a** 34 300 cm^3 (34.3 litres)   **b** 20.2 cm

39 3.63 cm   **40** 831 cm^3 8.79 cm   **41 a** 77.5 cm^3 **b** 1.07 cm

42 a 1.25 cm   **b** 98.1 cm^3 **c** 1.54 cm

Squares and square roots

Part 1 Squares

1 a 25   **b** 13   **c** 25   (ii) is correct

2 a 100   **b** 52   **c** 100   (ii) is correct

3 a 64   **b** 80   **c** 64   (ii) is correct

4 a 1   **b** 15   **c** 1   (ii) is correct

5 (i)   **6** (i)   **7** (ii)   **8** (i)   **9** (ii)

10 a $y^2 = (x + 2)^2$ **b** $y^2 = (3x - 4)^2$
     c $y^2 = (2x + 3z)^2$ **d** $y^2 = (a + b - c)^2$

11 a $y = (x + 2)^2$ **b** $y = (x - 5)^2$ **c** $y = (2x + 3)^2$ **d** $y = (x^2 - 7)^2$

12 a $y = (x - 4)^2$ **b** $y = x^2 - 4$ **c** $y = (x + 6)^2$ **d** $y = x^2 + 6$
     e $y = (z - x)^2$ **f** $y = z^2 - x$ **g** $y = (n + m)^2$ **h** $y = n^2 + m$

Squares and square roots

Part 2

1	a 36	b 36	c 36	Both are correct.
2	a 100	b 100	c 100	Both are correct.
3	a 16	b 16	c 16	Both are correct.
4	a 36	b 36	c 36	Both are correct.

5 Both are correct.　　**6** Both are correct.　　**7** Both are correct.

8 Both are correct.　　**9** Both are correct.

10 a $y^2 = (st)^2 = s^2t^2$　　　　**b** $y^2 = \left(\dfrac{4}{x}\right)^2 = \dfrac{16}{x^2}$

c $y^2 = \left(\dfrac{3p}{r}\right)^2 = \dfrac{9p^2}{r^2}$　　　**d** $y^2 = \left(\dfrac{b}{2a}\right)^2 = \dfrac{b^2}{4a^2}$

11 a $y = (6p)^2 = 36p^2$　　　　**b** $y = \left(\dfrac{p}{6}\right)^2 = \dfrac{p^2}{36}$

c $y = \left(\dfrac{3m}{n}\right)^2 = \dfrac{9m^2}{n^2}$　　　**d** $y = \left(\dfrac{\sqrt{x}}{2z}\right)^2 = \dfrac{x}{4z^2}$

12 a $y = \dfrac{x^2}{25}$　　**b** $y = \dfrac{x^2}{5}$　　**c** $y = 36x^2$　　**d** $y = 6x^2$

e $y = 4x$　　**f** $y = \dfrac{x}{9}$　　**g** $y = x^2$　　**h** $y = 28x^2$

Part 3 Square roots

1	a 5	b 4	c 3	(ii) is correct.
2	a 10	b 8	c 6	(ii) is correct.
3	a 12	b 13	c 5	(ii) is correct.

4 (ii)　　**5** (ii)　　**6** (i)　　**7** (i)　　**8** (ii)　　**9** (i)　　**10** (iii)

11 a $y = \sqrt{x + 4}$　**b** $y = \sqrt{x^2 + 4}$　**c** $y = \sqrt{9x - 16}$　**d** $y = \sqrt{4x^2 - 9}$

12 a $y = \sqrt{a^2 + 4}$　**b** $y = \sqrt{2a - 6}$　**c** $y = \sqrt{2a^2 + 9}$　**d** $y = \sqrt{a + 7}$

e $y = \sqrt{a - 4}$　**f** $y = \sqrt{a - 6}$　**g** $y = \sqrt{3a - 5}$　**h** $y = \sqrt{a^2 + 12}$

Part 4

1	a 6	b 3	c 2	Both are correct.
2	a 10	b 5	c 2	Both are correct.
3	a 12	b 6	c 2	Both are correct.

4 Both are correct.　　**5** Both are correct.　　**6** Both are correct.

7 Both are correct.　　**8** Both are correct.　　**9** Both are correct.

10 Both are correct.

Squares and square roots

11 **a** $y = \sqrt{m^2n^2} = mn$ **c** $y = \sqrt{\dfrac{m^2}{n^2}} = \dfrac{m}{n}$ **e** $y = \sqrt{\dfrac{4x^2}{9}} = \dfrac{2x}{3}$

    b $y = \sqrt{16x^2} = 4x$ **d** $y = \sqrt{\dfrac{m^2}{25}} = \dfrac{m}{5}$ **f** $y = \sqrt{\dfrac{49c^2}{4d^2}} = \dfrac{7c}{2d}$

12 **a** $y = 2x$ **c** $y = 5p$ **e** $y = 3\sqrt{x}$ **g** $y = \dfrac{\sqrt{x}}{2}$

    b $y = 3\sqrt{mn}$ **d** $y = \dfrac{6\sqrt{a}}{b}$ **f** $y = 2st$ **h** $y = \dfrac{\sqrt{x}}{3z}$

Part 5 Revision

1 $x = \sqrt{a + b}$ **18** $x = \sqrt{\dfrac{c}{d}}$ **35** $x = \dfrac{y^2}{4}$

2 $x = \sqrt{a - b}$ **19** $x = d\sqrt{c}$ **36** $x = \dfrac{y^2}{2}$

3 $x = \sqrt{ab}$ **20** $x = \dfrac{\sqrt{c}}{d}$ **37** $x = 4y^2$

4 $x = \sqrt{\dfrac{a}{b}}$ **21** $x = \sqrt{c - d}$ **38** $x = 2y^2$

5 $x = \sqrt{a^2 + b^2}$ **22** $x = \sqrt{c + d}$ **39** $x = y\sqrt{2}$

6 $x = \sqrt{a^2 - b^2}$ **23** $x = (c - d)^2$ **40** $x = (y - 2)^2$

7 $x = ab$ **24** $x = (c + d)^2$ **41** $x = \sqrt{y - 2}$

8 $x = \dfrac{a}{b}$ **25** $x = \dfrac{c^2}{d^2}$ **42** $x = (y + 2)^2$

9 $x = (a + b)^2$ **26** $x = c^2d^2$ **43** $x = \sqrt{y + 2}$

10 $x = (a - b)^2$ **27** $x = c^2 - d$ **44** $x = \sqrt{\dfrac{y - 5}{3}}$

11 $x = a^2b^2$ **28** $x = c^2 + d$ **45** $x = \sqrt{\dfrac{y + 3}{7}}$

12 $x = \dfrac{a^2}{b^2}$ **29** $x = \dfrac{c^2}{d}$ **46** $x = \sqrt{\dfrac{z - y}{2}}$

13 $x = \dfrac{a}{b}$ **30** $x = c^2d$ **47** $x = \left(\dfrac{z - y}{2}\right)^2$

14 $x = ab$ **31** $x = \sqrt{\dfrac{y}{2}}$ **48** $x = \dfrac{z^2}{4} - y$

15 $x = \sqrt{c - d}$ **32** $x = \dfrac{\sqrt{y}}{2}$ **49** $x = \dfrac{z^2}{2} - y$

16 $x = \sqrt{c + d}$ **33** $x = \sqrt{2y}$ **50** $x = 2z^2 - y$

17 $x = \sqrt{cd}$ **34** $x = 2\sqrt{y}$ **51** $x = 4z^2 - y$

Squares and square roots

52 $x = \dfrac{c}{2\pi}$ **55** $x = \sqrt{\dfrac{3V}{h}}$ **58** $x = \sqrt{y^2 - 2as}$

53 $x = \sqrt{\dfrac{A}{\pi}}$ **56** $x = \sqrt{\dfrac{e}{R}}$ **59** $x = \dfrac{t^2 g}{36}$

54 $x = \sqrt{\dfrac{V}{h}}$ **57** $x = \sqrt{h^2 - y^2}$ **60** $x = \sqrt{\dfrac{k}{F}}$

Numerical rearrangement of scientific formulae

Part 1

	a		b		c		d		e	
1	18		9		5					
2	6		6		8					
3	45		2		5					
4	72		5		3		4			
5	12		16		14					
6	32		8		11		6			
7	6		$\frac{2}{3}$		10		$3\frac{1}{3}$			
8	6		10		40					
9	24		15		6		4			
10	13		9		16		4			
11	7		8		8		2			
12	78		3		4		8			
13	36		6		1		7		7	
14	60		6		2		7			
15	$7\frac{1}{2}$		$13\frac{1}{2}$		2		$7\frac{1}{2}$			
16	4		75							
17	8		54							
18	18		160		10					
19	18		9		5		3			
20	180		3							
21	12		90		4					
22	459		$3\frac{1}{3}$		6		8			
23	420		2							
24	3		$1\frac{1}{5}$		3		6			

Part 2 (Answers given to 3 significant figures)

1	3.07	**6**	5.21	**11**	3.99	**16**	732	**21**	50.1
2	4.15	**7**	1.66	**12**	6.97	**17**	85.1	**22**	7.99
3	3.30	**8**	1.36	**13**	6.70	**18**	88.2	**23**	5.83
4	6.38	**9**	2.69	**14**	2.70	**19**	23.1	**24**	1.39
5	60.7	**10**	1.67	**15**	11.2	**20**	10.2		

Flow diagrams and rearrangement of formulae
Part 1

1 $y = 3x + 6$

$x = \dfrac{y - 6}{3}$

2 $y = 4x - 8$

$x = \dfrac{y + 8}{4}$

3 $y = 2(x + 7)$

$x = \dfrac{y}{2} - 7$

4 $y = 3(x - 5)$

$x = \dfrac{y}{3} + 5$

5 $y = \dfrac{x}{2} + 3$

$x = 2(y - 3)$

6 $y = \dfrac{x + 3}{2}$

$x = 2y - 3$

7 $y = \dfrac{x}{5} - 1$

$x = 5(y + 1)$

8 $y = \dfrac{x - 1}{5}$

$x = 5y + 1$

9 $y = x^2 + 7$

$x = \sqrt{y - 7}$

10 $y = x^2 - 2$

$x = \sqrt{y + 2}$

11 $y = (x + 7)^2$

$x = \sqrt{y} - 7$

12 $y = (x - 2)^2$

$x = \sqrt{y} + 2$

13 $y = 3x^2$

$x = \sqrt{\dfrac{y}{3}}$

14 $y = \dfrac{x^2}{5}$

$x = \sqrt{5y}$

15 $y = (6x)^2$

$x = \dfrac{\sqrt{y}}{6}$

16 $y = \left(\dfrac{x}{8}\right)^2$

$x = 8\sqrt{y}$

17 $y = \sqrt{x} + 3$

$x = (y - 3)^2$

18 $y = \sqrt{x - 9}$

$x = y^2 + 9$

19 $y = \sqrt{3x}$

$x = \dfrac{y^2}{3}$

20 $y = \dfrac{\sqrt{x}}{7}$

$x = (7y)^2$

21 $y = \dfrac{x^2 + 2}{5}$

$x = \sqrt{5y - 2}$

22 $y = \dfrac{(x + 2)^2}{5}$

$x = \sqrt{5y} - 2$

23 $y = \left(\dfrac{x}{5} + 2\right)^2$

$x = 5(\sqrt{y} - 2)$

24 $y = \sqrt{\dfrac{x - 4}{2}}$

$x = 2y^2 + 4$

25 $y = \dfrac{\sqrt{x} + 7}{3}$

$x = (3y - 7)^2$

26 $y = \dfrac{3(x + 6)}{4}$

$x = \dfrac{4y}{3} - 6$

27 $y = 2\left(\dfrac{x}{8} - 5\right)$

$x = 8\left(\dfrac{y}{2} + 5\right)$

28 $y = \sqrt{x^2 + 9}$

$x = \sqrt{y^2 - 9}$

29 $y = \left(\dfrac{\sqrt{x} - 2}{3}\right)^2$

$x = (3\sqrt{y} + 2)^2$

30 $y = \dfrac{7(x + 6)}{7} - 6$

$x = \dfrac{7(y + 6)}{7} - 6$

$\therefore\ x = y$

Flow diagrams and rearrangement of formulae

Part 2

1 $x = \dfrac{y - 3}{2}$

2 $x = \dfrac{y - 7}{5}$

3 $x = \dfrac{y + 1}{4}$

4 $x = \dfrac{2y + 7}{3}$

5 $x = \dfrac{y + 9}{6}$

6 $x = \dfrac{3y - 2}{8}$

7 $x = \dfrac{y - 3a}{a}$

8 $x = \dfrac{2 + ab}{a}$

9 $x = \dfrac{b - a}{a}$

10 $x = 2a$

11 $x = 2(a + 3)$

12 $x = 4(a - 2)$

13 $x = \dfrac{4a}{3}$

14 $x = \frac{4}{3}(a + 2)$

15 $x = \frac{4}{3}(a - 1)$

16 $x = 3y - 2$

17 $x = 3(y - 2)$

18 $x = 4y + 5$

19 $x = 4(y + 5)$

20 $x = ac - b$

21 $x = c(a - b)$

22 $x = 3z + y$

23 $x = \sqrt{y + 3}$

24 $x = \sqrt{y - 9}$

25 $x = \sqrt{b - a}$

26 $x = \sqrt{a + b}$

27 $x = \sqrt{z^2 - y^2}$

28 $x = \sqrt{3y}$

29 $x = \sqrt{7(z + 2)}$

30 $x = \sqrt{8(a + b)}$

31 $x = \sqrt{\dfrac{y}{3}}$

32 $x = \sqrt{\dfrac{z + 2}{5}}$

33 $x = \sqrt{\dfrac{a + b}{7}}$

34 $x = \sqrt{\dfrac{a - b}{2}}$

35 $x = \sqrt{\dfrac{2 + y}{3}}$

36 $x = \sqrt{\dfrac{a^2 - 1}{5}}$

37 $x = \sqrt{y} - 3$

38 $x = \sqrt{y} + 4$

39 $x = \sqrt{b} - a$

40 $x = 2(\sqrt{y} + z)$

41 $x = 4(\sqrt{y} - 1)$

42 $x = 6(\sqrt{3} + p)$

43 $x = \dfrac{\sqrt{y} + 5}{2}$

44 $x = \dfrac{\sqrt{b} - a}{3}$

45 $x = \dfrac{\sqrt{p} + n}{m}$

46 $x = y^2$

47 $x = (y + z)^2$

48 $x = (y + 2)^2$

49 $x = y^2 + 2$

50 $x = (b - a)^2$

51 $x = b^2 - a$

52 $x = (m + n)^2$

53 $x = n^2 + m$

54 $x = p^2 q^2$

55 $x = pq^2$

56 $x = 9y^2$

57 $x = 3y^2$

58 $x = \sqrt{\dfrac{3(n - m)}{2}}$

59 $x = \sqrt{3b} + a$

60 $x = \sqrt{bc^2 + 2}$

Flow diagrams and rearrangement of formulae
Part 3

1 $x = \dfrac{4a}{3}$

2 $x = c$

3 $x = \dfrac{m}{5}$

4 $x = \dfrac{p}{2}$

5 $x = \dfrac{8a}{7}$

6 $x = \dfrac{3b}{2}$

7 $x = \dfrac{7q}{5}$

8 $x = \dfrac{5}{3m}$

9 $x = \dfrac{b}{6}$

10 $x = \dfrac{6 - 6a}{7}$

11 $x = \dfrac{7c}{9a}$

12 $x = \dfrac{4q - 5p}{2p}$

13 $x = \dfrac{p - q}{2a}$

14 $x = \dfrac{a + 2b}{5m}$

15 $x = 8p + 3q$

16 $x = \dfrac{4a + 3b}{2a}$

17 $x = \dfrac{m}{3}$

18 $x = \dfrac{q}{5}$

19 $x = \dfrac{c}{3a}$

20 $x = \dfrac{6c - ad}{2a}$

21 $x = \dfrac{7a}{3}$

22 $x = 8c$

23 $x = -m$

24 $x = 2a$

25 $x = \frac{1}{2}\sqrt{3a}$

26 $x = \sqrt{\dfrac{2c - 3ab}{a}}$

27 $x = \sqrt{\dfrac{3mn + n^2}{4m}}$

28 $x = \sqrt{\dfrac{3m}{p}}$

29 $x = \sqrt{\dfrac{c}{2a}}$

30 $x = \sqrt{a}$

31 $x = \dfrac{m}{\sqrt{2}}$

32 $x = \frac{1}{5}\sqrt{p}$

33 $x = \sqrt{\dfrac{2}{3a}}$

34 $x = \dfrac{a}{\sqrt{2}}$

Flow diagrams and rearrangement of formulae

Part 4

1. $x = \dfrac{c}{a - b}$

2. $x = \dfrac{c}{a + b}$

3. $x = \dfrac{n}{m + 2}$

4. $x = \dfrac{3}{y - z}$

5. $x = \dfrac{c - b}{a - b}$

6. $x = \dfrac{r + s}{p - q}$

7. $x = \dfrac{3s}{y + z}$

8. $x = \dfrac{3a + 2v}{3 - v}$

9. $x = \dfrac{4r - st}{s - 4}$

10. $x = \dfrac{a + 2b}{a - b}$

11. $x = \dfrac{m + n}{a + b + c}$

12. $x = \dfrac{2k + 3m}{m - n + 2}$

13. $x = \sqrt{\dfrac{c}{a - b}}$

14. $x = \sqrt{\dfrac{3}{m - n}}$

15. $x = \sqrt{\dfrac{b + c}{b - c}}$

16. $x = \sqrt{\dfrac{c}{a - b}}$

17. $x = \sqrt{\dfrac{d}{1 - c}}$

18. $x = \sqrt{\dfrac{bc}{a - b}}$

19. $x = \sqrt{\dfrac{m}{1 - m}}$

20. $x = \sqrt{\dfrac{b - a}{c}}$

21. $x = \sqrt{\dfrac{b}{a - c}}$

22. $x = \sqrt{\dfrac{1}{b - a}}$

23. $x = \sqrt{\dfrac{n}{m - n}}$

24. $x = \sqrt{\dfrac{6c}{3a - 2b}}$

25. $x = \sqrt{\dfrac{3c + 4d}{6(p - 2q)}}$

26. $x = \sqrt{\dfrac{b}{a - 1}}$

27. $x = \sqrt{\dfrac{2m}{m - 9}}$

28. $x = \sqrt{\dfrac{b}{a^2 - b^2}}$

29. $x = \dfrac{a}{1 - b^2}$

30. $x = \dfrac{n^2 + 3}{m^2}$

31. $x = \dfrac{a}{1 - b^2}$

32. $x = \sqrt{\dfrac{3}{m^2 - n^2}}$

33. $x = \left(\dfrac{d - b}{a - c}\right)^2$

34. $x = \left(\dfrac{n - q}{m - p}\right)^2$

35. $x = \left(\dfrac{y + z}{2 - a}\right)^2$

36. $x = \left(\dfrac{2(a + 2b)}{b - a}\right)^2$

37. $x = \left(\dfrac{bc}{b - a}\right)^2$

38. $x = \left(\dfrac{a}{m + n}\right)^2$

39. $x = \left(\dfrac{b - a}{2}\right)^2$

40. $x = \dfrac{bq}{p}$

Flow diagrams and rearrangement of formulae

Part 5

1 $i = \dfrac{v}{R}$

2 $r = \dfrac{C}{2\pi}$

3 $h = \dfrac{E}{mg}$

4 $h = \dfrac{V}{lb}$

5 $V = \dfrac{kT}{P}$

6 $T = \dfrac{100I}{PR}$

7 $h = \dfrac{3V}{x^2}$

8 $S = \dfrac{RA}{L}$

9 $t = \dfrac{v - u}{a}$

10 $s = \dfrac{v^2 - u^2}{2a}$

11 $x = 3m - y - z$

12 $h = \dfrac{s}{2\pi r} - r$

13 $t = \dfrac{L - L_0}{\alpha L_0}$

14 $i = \sqrt{\dfrac{w}{R}}$

15 $r = \sqrt{\dfrac{A}{\pi}}$

16 $x = \sqrt{\dfrac{V}{h}}$

17 $v = \sqrt{\dfrac{2E}{m}}$

18 $i = \sqrt{\dfrac{p}{Rt}}$

19 $r = \sqrt{\dfrac{3V}{\pi h}}$

20 $u = \sqrt{v^2 - 2as}$

21 $h = \dfrac{v^2}{2g}$

22 $h = \dfrac{2D^2}{3}$

23 $L = \dfrac{t^2 g}{4\pi^2}$

24 $L = \dfrac{2s}{n} - A$

25 $v = \dfrac{2s}{t} - u$

26 $a = \dfrac{2(s - ut)}{t^2}$

27 $n = \dfrac{2s}{A + L}$

28 $t = \dfrac{2s}{u + v}$

29 $s = \dfrac{Rr}{r - R}$

30 $u = \dfrac{fv}{v - f}$

Fractions in Algebra

Equivalence
Multiplication
Division
Addition and subtraction

Equivalence

1

a $\dfrac{3x}{4x}$ **h** $\dfrac{15a}{9c}$ **o** $\dfrac{3y}{xy}$ **v** $\dfrac{xy}{y^2}$

b $\dfrac{2a}{3a}$ **i** $\dfrac{8x}{20y}$ **p** $\dfrac{6y}{2xy}$ **w** $\dfrac{ab}{b^2}$

c $\dfrac{3m}{5m}$ **j** $\dfrac{9a}{6a}$ **q** $\dfrac{8n}{2mn}$ **x** $\dfrac{mn}{n^2}$

d $\dfrac{4n}{7n}$ **k** $\dfrac{8x}{10x}$ **r** $\dfrac{9t}{6st}$ **y** $\dfrac{4ab}{6b^2}$

e $\dfrac{4}{6a}$ **l** $\dfrac{9m}{21m}$ **s** $\dfrac{10y}{8xy}$ **z** $\dfrac{8x^2y}{6xy^2}$

f $\dfrac{4b}{6a}$ **m** $\dfrac{4z}{10z}$ **t** $\dfrac{6n}{4mn}$

g $\dfrac{12x}{8y}$ **n** $\dfrac{6a}{14a}$ **u** $\dfrac{16q}{2pq}$

2

a $\dfrac{y}{4}$ **h** $2f$ **o** $2b$ **v** $\dfrac{a^2}{c}$

b $\dfrac{n}{3}$ **i** $\dfrac{x}{y}$ **p** $\dfrac{n}{3}$ **w** $\dfrac{x}{2y}$

c $\dfrac{4a}{5}$ **j** $\dfrac{a}{bc}$ **q** $\dfrac{2r}{3}$ **x** $\dfrac{3y}{2z}$

d $\dfrac{2y}{3x}$ **k** $\dfrac{m}{2}$ **r** $\dfrac{5k}{h}$ **y** $\dfrac{3p^3q^2}{2}$

e $\dfrac{8a}{3d}$ **l** $\dfrac{x}{3}$ **s** $\dfrac{2m}{3}$ **z** $\dfrac{x^2}{z^2}$

f $\dfrac{p}{2r}$ **m** $\dfrac{p}{3}$ **t** $\dfrac{2y}{3x}$

g $2n$ **n** $\dfrac{x}{y}$ **u** $\dfrac{3tu}{2s}$

Multiplication

1 $\dfrac{2a}{3b}$

2 $\dfrac{4c}{5d}$

3 $\dfrac{6m}{7n}$

4 $\dfrac{10a}{3b}$

5 $\dfrac{8m}{3n}$

6 $\dfrac{ab}{12}$

7 $\dfrac{6ab}{35}$

8 $\dfrac{8}{15ab}$

9 $\dfrac{4cd}{15mn}$

10 $\dfrac{4a}{3}$

11 $\dfrac{10p}{3}$

12 $\dfrac{x^2}{y^2}$

13 $\dfrac{3x^2}{2y^2}$

14 $\dfrac{8m^2}{15n^2}$

15 $\dfrac{a^3}{6b^2}$

16 $\dfrac{6x^3}{5y^3}$

17 $\dfrac{a^4}{b^3}$

18 $\dfrac{6p^4}{5r^3}$

19 $\dfrac{3b^4}{8c^3}$

20 $\dfrac{3y^4}{2x^3}$

21 $\dfrac{5m^2}{6n^3}$

22 $\dfrac{3r^3}{8s^3}$

23 $\dfrac{3m}{n^5}$

24 $\dfrac{20x^4}{9y^2}$

25 $\dfrac{2b}{3a}$

26 $\dfrac{3y}{4z}$

27 $\dfrac{p}{4q}$

28 $\dfrac{n^2}{2m}$

29 $\dfrac{3a}{2c}$

30 $\dfrac{5z}{3y}$

31 $\dfrac{6a}{5b}$

32 $\dfrac{2b}{3c}$

33 $\dfrac{9m}{8}$

34 $\dfrac{12}{y}$

35 $\dfrac{3x}{2}$

36 $1\frac{2}{3}$

37 1

38 $\dfrac{3x}{2}$

39 $\dfrac{3x}{4}$

40 $2b$

41 $\dfrac{2y}{z}$

42 $2m$

43 pq

44 $\dfrac{2a^2}{3}$

45 $\dfrac{a^2}{2}$

46 $\dfrac{p^3}{2}$

47 s^3

48 $\dfrac{a^2}{d^2}$

49 y^2

50 $\dfrac{4m^2}{n^3}$

Division

1 $\dfrac{3x}{2y}$

2 $\dfrac{4a}{3b}$

3 $\dfrac{d}{4c}$

4 $\dfrac{6n}{5m}$

5 $\dfrac{bx}{ay}$

6 $\dfrac{4np}{9mq}$

7 $\dfrac{4c}{3d}$

8 $\dfrac{4y}{z}$

9 $\dfrac{6x}{a}$

10 $\dfrac{m}{2n}$

11 $\dfrac{3b}{2d}$

12 $\dfrac{2x}{y}$

13 xy

14 $\dfrac{3}{a}$

15 $\dfrac{6}{ab}$

16 $\dfrac{2x^2}{3}$

17 $\dfrac{m^2}{4}$

18 $6n$

19 $\dfrac{ad}{bc}$

20 $\dfrac{xy^2}{2}$

21 $\dfrac{n^2}{3m}$

22 $\dfrac{s^2}{t^2}$

23 1

24 $\dfrac{s^2}{t^2}$

25 $\dfrac{3b^3}{5}$

26 $\dfrac{6p^2}{q^2}$

27 $\dfrac{3x}{2y^2}$

28 $\dfrac{2p^2}{q^2}$

29 $\dfrac{2m^3}{n^2}$

30 $\dfrac{3x^2}{2y^2}$

31 a^2b^2

32 $\dfrac{x}{5}$

33 $\dfrac{x}{4y}$

34 $\dfrac{3m}{n^2}$

35 $\dfrac{q}{2}$

36 1

Addition and subtraction

Part 1

1 $\dfrac{a + b}{2}$

2 $\dfrac{a - b}{2}$

3 $\dfrac{x + y}{3}$

4 $\dfrac{x - y}{3}$

5 $\dfrac{a + b}{x}$

6 $\dfrac{a - b}{x}$

7 $\dfrac{m + 2}{a}$

8 $\dfrac{n - 3}{b}$

9 $\dfrac{ab + 3}{z}$

10 $\dfrac{1 + pq}{a}$

11 $\dfrac{9}{a}$

12 $\dfrac{4}{x}$

13 $\dfrac{7}{m}$

14 $\dfrac{11x}{2}$

15 $\dfrac{4y}{n}$

16 $\dfrac{6a}{x}$

17 $\dfrac{x + 1}{2}$

18 $\dfrac{x + 2}{4}$

19 $\dfrac{y - 2}{4}$

20 $\dfrac{a + 2b}{4}$

21 $\dfrac{m + 2n}{6}$

22 $\dfrac{c - 3d}{9}$

23 $\dfrac{x + 3y}{12}$

24 $\dfrac{3x + y}{12}$

25 $\dfrac{3m + n}{6}$

26 $\dfrac{4a + 1}{8}$

27 $\dfrac{a + 4}{8}$

28 $\dfrac{4p - 1}{12}$

29 $\dfrac{p - 4}{12}$

30 $\dfrac{4a + b}{6}$

31 $\dfrac{6x - y}{4}$

32 $\dfrac{6x + y}{9}$

33 $\dfrac{9m - 5n}{12}$

34 $\dfrac{15p - 7q}{9}$

35 $\dfrac{8x + 7y}{12}$

36 $\dfrac{2x + 3y}{6}$

37 $\dfrac{3x + 2y}{6}$

38 $\dfrac{2a - 5b}{10}$

39 $\dfrac{5m - 3n}{15}$

40 $\dfrac{4p + 15q}{6}$

41 $\dfrac{9s - 8t}{12}$

42 $\dfrac{10a - 9b}{12}$

43 $\dfrac{12s + 10t}{15}$

44 $\dfrac{2ab - 9cd}{12}$

45 $\dfrac{7ab}{12}$

46 $\dfrac{45x}{14}$

47 $\dfrac{5p + 3}{3}$

48 $\dfrac{5s + 6}{2}$

49 $\dfrac{x + 4y}{4}$

50 $\dfrac{3a - 5b}{5}$

51 $\dfrac{4x - 3y}{4}$

52 $\dfrac{10m + n}{5}$

53 $\dfrac{3b + 2}{ab}$

54 $\dfrac{4d - 3}{cd}$

55 $\dfrac{1 + 2n}{mn}$

56 $\dfrac{x + 2z}{yz}$

57 $\dfrac{3q - r}{pq}$

58 $\dfrac{a + 1}{a^2}$

59 $\dfrac{4 - 3b}{b^2}$

60 $\dfrac{m - n}{n^2}$

Addition and subtraction

Part 2

1 $\dfrac{5x}{6}$

2 $\dfrac{8y}{15}$

3 $\dfrac{13z}{10}$

4 $\dfrac{11x}{15}$

5 $\dfrac{23a}{21}$

6 $\dfrac{c}{10}$

7 $\dfrac{41m}{24}$

8 $\dfrac{p}{12}$

9 $\dfrac{29q}{20}$

10 $\dfrac{5s}{24}$

11 $\dfrac{8a + 3b}{12}$

12 $\dfrac{25c - 6d}{10}$

13 $\dfrac{4e + 7f}{14}$

14 $\dfrac{12g - 15h}{20}$

15 $\dfrac{25i + 12j}{20}$

16 $\dfrac{18m - 14n}{21}$

17 $\dfrac{8p + 15q}{20}$

18 $\dfrac{x - 6y}{8}$

19 $\dfrac{10y + 3z}{12}$

20 $\dfrac{16a - 15b}{18}$

21 $\dfrac{3x + 2}{6}$

22 $\dfrac{7y + 4}{8}$

23 $\dfrac{2z + 6y - 3}{4}$

24 $\dfrac{9a + 2}{10}$

25 $\dfrac{11s + 6}{6}$

26 $\dfrac{7t - 9}{12}$

27 $\dfrac{7u + 2}{10}$

28 $\dfrac{7x + 16}{12}$

29 $\dfrac{7y + 24}{24}$

30 $\dfrac{14z - 3}{15}$

31 $\dfrac{7x + 10}{12}$

32 $\dfrac{11x + 22}{15}$

33 $\dfrac{13y + 9}{18}$

34 $\dfrac{8y + 11}{30}$

35 $\dfrac{7z - 11}{24}$

36 $\dfrac{13a + 2}{12}$

37 $\dfrac{2a - 37}{24}$

38 $\dfrac{m - 14}{18}$

39 $\dfrac{29p - 2}{60}$

40 $\dfrac{7}{36}$